The
Modern Theory
of
MOLECULAR
STRUCTURE

By

BERNARD PULLMAN
Professor at the Faculté des Sciences of Paris

Translated by

David Antin

DOVER PUBLICATIONS, INC.

NEW YORK

N.C. 62-6845

Manufactured in the United States of America

Dover Publications, Inc.
180 Varick Street
New York 14, N. Y.

Contents

Introduction

The present theories of molecular structure are based on the principles of wave mechanics, which employs analytical methods requiring very complex mathematical techniques. But the fundamental ideas and principal results can be described in non-mathematical language and thus made accessible to a large public. In this book our aim has been precisely to present a general exposition of the modern conceptions of molecular structure as simply as possible and without mathematical development. The non-specialist reader will therefore be able to obtain some general conceptions that can be assimilated without too great difficulty in this important area of present-day science. For those wishing a deeper understanding of the subject a bibliography is placed at the end of this work.

CHAPTER ONE

The Wave Function and Wave Equations

1. A Short History of the Theories of Molecular Structure.
The development of the modern theories of molecular structure
can be divided into three general periods:

a) the first period, from the acceptance of the atomic theory
at the beginning of the nineteenth century to the discovery of
the fine structure of the atom towards the end of the century;

b) the second period, from the discovery of the electron to
the appearance of wave mechanics and covering the two first
decades of the twentieth century;

c) the third period, in which the theories held today received
definitive elaboration, beginning with Louis de Broglie's discovery of the wave nature of matter.

The end of the eighteenth century and the beginning of the
nineteenth saw the definitive establishment of the atomic theory
of matter (the works of Dalton, Avogadro's hypothesis) as well
as the principal empirical laws governing the formation of
molecules by atoms: Lavoisier's law of the conservation of
mass, the gravimetric laws (the laws of definite proportions,
of multiple proportions, of proportional numbers) and the
volumetric laws of chemical combination. Almost at the
same time there arose the outlines of a theory of molecular
structure, the object of which was to account for the manner in
which different atoms or groups of atoms forming simple
compounds were bound together in space and to explain the
nature of the forces ensuring the stability of the structure.
The first in date of these attempts was *the electrostatic theory* of
Davy (1806) and Berzelius (1812). According to this theory,
each molecule was composed of a certain number of atoms or
radicals (particularly stable groupings of atoms, e.g. NH_3,
HCl, SO_3, etc.) held together by the electrostatic attraction
between two charges of opposite sign. According to Davy
these charges were developed only when two appropriate substances approached each other; according to Berzelius the

1

existence of the charges was prior to this and was to be found in the isolated atoms or radicals.

This is an essentially *dualistic* theory, in which the complex molecules are considered as products of a simple juxtaposition of more basic elements.　This conception was translated into the notation used.　One wrote, for example:

$$SO_3 + K_2O = SO_3 \cdot K_2O$$

a troublesome and obviously defective notation, since the same compound could be produced in several different ways.　Moreover, this electrostatic conception could obviously not be applied to homonuclear diatomic molecules such as H_2, F_2, etc.

In spite of the obvious inadequacies of the Davy-Berzelius theories, they seemed able to hold on in inorganic chemistry. It was very different in organic chemistry, where Dumas in 1834 showed that it was necessary to replace the dualistic theory with a *monistic* theory that would consider the molecule as a unique entity in which it was no longer possible to distinguish the individuality of the component radicals.　Dumas arrived at this notion through his work on substitution reactions, in which he showed that an atom of chlorine, considered negative, was capable of replacing hydrogen, which was considered positive, in carbon derivatives (such as acetic acid) without producing a *significant change* in the molecular properties.　This state of affairs gave every evidence of being in direct contradiction to the theories of Davy and Berzelius.

Dumas' conceptions are practically the basis of the concept of valence and all structural chemistry.　In effect, his theory made it possible to attribute to each element a certain capacity for combination or substitution, which was considered its *valence*.　If hydrogen is chosen as the base of the scale, i.e. if the valence of one is assigned to hydrogen, oxygen must be assigned a valence of two, nitrogen a valence of three, carbon a valence of four, etc.

Moreover, complex molecules can be considered as deriving from *molecule types* such as HCl, H_2O, NH_3, CH_4, etc., which eventually makes it possible to assign a fixed valence to simple groups of elements in a manner reminiscent of Berzelius' radicals; in this case, however, the groups possess only a hypothetical existence.　For example, sulfuric acid (H_2SO_4)

can be considered as deriving from H_2O, with the atom of O replaced by the group SO_4, which is therefore bivalent. It was soon observed, however, that in inorganic chemistry elements were frequently characterized by several different valences; and by the time the periodic system had been established (Mendeleyev, 1870), it appeared that the maximum valence of an element depended on its place in the system. In organic chemistry constancy of valence seemed to be the rule.

As long as one assumed with Berzelius that the molecule was formed by two ions held together by electrostatic attraction, there was no need to ascribe a definite spatial arrangement to these ions. It was otherwise with Dumas' theory, which distinctly suggested that the atoms were *bound* in a definite manner into the molecule. It is actually to Dumas that we owe the *developed formula* and that important chemical symbol —, the dash placed between two linked atoms. Brilliant development of these concepts led to the stereochemical theories of van't Hoff and Le Bel (1874), in particular to their model for carbon. According to this model the four valences of this atom are directed toward the four apices of a regular tetrahedron, the center of which is occupied by the carbon itself. The simple C—C bond consists of two such tetrahedrons coupled by a common apex; a double bond consists of two such tetrahedrons coupled by a common side; and a triple bond consists of two such tetrahedrons coupled by a common face. We shall see further on what part of these conceptions has been retained and what discarded by modern theories.

Although the structural theory was certainly better adapted to describe the phenomena of organic chemistry than the electrostatic theory, it still presented serious deficiencies. It was incapable of offering any precise information concerning the nature of the forces responsible for the stability of the molecules. It was purely descriptive and its symbols (e.g. the dash between atoms) had a merely formal significance.

The discovery of the fine structure of the atom (J. J. Thomson, Rutherford, etc.) inaugurated a new era in the theory of molecular structure. At about the end of the last and beginning of the present century it was, in effect, established that the atom was not, as had long been believed, an indivisible unit of matter, but that it possessed in itself a complex structure. The atom was seen as composed of a positively charged nucleus, in which almost all of the atomic mass was concentrated, and about which a certain number of negatively charged particles of a very minute mass called *electrons* gravitated. Each element was characterized by a definite number of these electrons. Since the atoms were electrically neutral the charge of the nucleus was equal to the total charge of the electrons.

In 1916 Bohr presented a theory of atomic structure that appeared to revolutionize the conceptions current at the time. According to his theory the electrons in the atom could only travel in certain orbits with well-defined energy levels. Circulation within these orbits did not involve any exchange of energy with the outside world. On the other hand, the movement of an electron from its permissible orbit to another orbit was effected by the emission or absorption of energy (in the form of radiation). The frequency ν of the light produced was related to the variation of energy Δw by the equation

$$\nu = \frac{\Delta w}{h}$$

where h is a universal constant known as Planck's constant. Only certain frequencies, then, were permissible.

Though it introduced several apparently arbitrary concepts, Bohr's theory proved very fruitful in interpreting, even quantitatively, the structure of simple atoms, particularly hydrogen. This then appeared to open up a new path for studies of molecular structure as well. Surprisingly, the extension of this theory to molecules resulted in a complete setback. The reasons for this will be seen later.

Nevertheless, certain qualitative attempts to perfect the theories of molecular structure were made at about the same time (1916). These were essentially the result of the work of Kossel, Lewis and Langmuir, whose proposals may be summarized as follows: the chemical bond is of an electronic nature. It is the result of the coupling of lone electrons belonging to the outermost shells of the linked atoms. The coupling occurs in doublets: two electrons belonging to two different atoms can unite to form a *binding pair* shared by the two atoms. A pair of this type constitutes a single chemical bond; two pairs constitute a double bond; and three pairs, a triple bond. A pair is *inert* with respect to the formation of further bonds. Moreover, the remarkable stability of the rare gases, which is due to the fact that their outermost electron shell (containing two electrons in the case of helium and eight in the other gases) is complete, suggests that each atom in a molecule tends to surround itself with four electron pairs (shared or not), which form the surrounding octet. Such an arrangement when realized assures the stability of the molecule.

Let us consider the example of two atoms of chlorine, each of which possesses seven electrons in its peripheral shell. When two such atoms unite to form the molecule Cl_2 each of the atoms is surrounded by an *electron octet*. This phenomenon is defined precisely by the notation proposed by Lewis; the electrons are here indicated by dots, an isolated dot represents a lone electron, i.e. a *free valence*. Two dots grouped together indicate a doublet. The combination of two chlorine atoms can then be represented as:

$$:\overset{..}{\underset{..}{Cl}}\cdot \ + \ \cdot\overset{..}{\underset{..}{Cl}}: \ \rightarrow \ :\overset{..}{\underset{..}{Cl}}:\overset{..}{\underset{..}{Cl}}:$$

Since the saturation of the valences is complete, formation of Cl_3 will not occur.

This group of ideas, which we shall analyze no further, proved very fruitful in the interpretation of a great many chemical observations. In particular, the description of the chemical bond in terms of one or more pairs shared by the bound atoms constituted a considerable advance beyond the previous conceptions. Still, the purely formal nature of the description remained. In effect, the nature of the forces holding the pair together and ensuring the bond between the atoms continued to be ignored. At first sight the formation of a bond by the union of two particles possessing the same electrical charge in itself appeared astonishing. It was the development of wave mechanics which initiated the third stage in the evolution of the theories of molecular structure and provided a fundamental explanation of the nature of the chemical bond, an explanation which, among other things, confirmed the accuracy of some of the previous conceptions.

2. The Bases of the Present Theories. The starting point for the theories now accepted is the fundamental hypothesis put forth in 1924 by Louis de Broglie, according to which each electron is to be associated with a wave the wave length λ of which is connected to the magnitude of its movement p by the relation

$$\lambda = \frac{h}{p} = \frac{h}{mv}$$

where m is the mass of the electron, v its velocity and h the Planck constant, which we have already encountered in Bohr's formula and which is equal to 6.6242×10^{-27} ergs/sec. The accuracy of this hypothesis was authoritatively demonstrated in 1927 by the discovery of the phenomenon of electronic diffraction.

This double nature, corpuscular and undulatory, of the electron was no longer reconcilable with the classical Newtonian conceptions which represented an electron as a punctiform corpuscle that described a definite trajectory with a known velocity at every moment. This precise localization had to be replaced with a more statistical conception that indicated the probability of finding an electron at various points in space. In the new mechanics that were born with de Broglie's hypothesis it is assumed that *all that it is possible to know about the kinetic state of a material corpuscle leads to a certain mathematical function of the coordinates and time:*

$$\Psi(x,y,z,t)$$

This is the wave function that corresponds to the corpuscle under consideration.[1] The quantity Ψ^2 represents the *probability of the presence* of the corpuscle at the point of intersection of the coordinates x,y,z at the moment t. Since the total probability of finding the corpuscle must be equal to unity, this probability interpretation imposes the following condition, called the normalization condition, on the wave function:

$$\int |\Psi|^2 dt = 1$$

[1] The wave function Ψ is a complex function, i.e. it contains the imaginary number $i = \sqrt{-1}$. If i is replaced with $-i$ in the function, one obtains the conjugated function Ψ^* and the product $\Psi\Psi^*$ is always real. This is then written $|\Psi|^2$.

Given these conventions it is no longer possible to say that an electron will be located at a certain moment at a given point, but one must say that it is more or less probable that it will be found at one point rather than another. In a more figurative fashion it might be represented as spread out in a cloud the density of which at each point would represent the probability of its presence at that point; thus, instead of saying that there is a 1/5 probability of finding the electron at a given point, one might say that everything acts as though 1/5 of the electron were located at that point. One frequently has recourse to such convenient language, but it is important to remember what it really means.

The wave function of a corpuscle is obtained as the solution of the corresponding wave equations. It is not our intention and it is not possible to enter here into the details of the symbolism concerning the derivation of this equation or the methods permitting the solution of the equation.[2] We shall merely mention here that *this equation can be considered as a translation into a new form of the classical law of the conservation of energy.* For a corpuscle in a constant field (the potential of which is independent of time)—the only case we will consider here—this equation has the form

$$\Delta\psi + \frac{8\pi^2 m}{h^2}(E - V)\psi = 0$$

in which m is the mass of the corpuscle, h is Planck's constant, V the potential energy of the system, the symbol

$$\Delta = \frac{\partial^2}{\partial x^2} + \frac{\partial^2}{\partial y^2} + \frac{\partial^2}{\partial z^2}$$

and the function ψ that acts here is the orbital portion (depending only on the coordinates) of the wave function.

This equation, which is known as *Schrödinger's equation*, is then an equation with linear partial derivatives of the second order. This type of equation does not have a solution that satisfies the general conditions of the wave function (i.e. that it must be continuous, uniform, finite throughout the area of

[2] Readers interested in the mathematical aspects of this problem will find a detailed account in B. Pullman and A. Pullman, *Les théories électroniques de la chimie organique*, Masson, Paris (1952).

localization of the corpuscle and null at the limits of this domain) except for certain values of the constant E. These values are the *eigenvalues* (Trans.: characteristic values) of the equation and represent the *permissible energies* of the corpuscle. One of the great advantages of the new mechanics consists precisely of the fact that the quantification of the energy derives naturally from the mathematical form of these equations and is not introduced in an arbitrary fashion as, for example, in Bohr's model of the atom.

There are one or more functions $\psi(x,y,z)$ satisfying the necessary conditions for each permissible energy value; these functions are called *eigenfunctions* (Trans.: characteristic functions) and describe the corpuscle in that energy state.

All that has preceded is readily extended to the case of a group of corpuscles.

This group of conceptions forms the basis of the present electronic theories of molecular structure. The following chapters of this book will deal more precisely with the application of these theories to various aspects of the problem. Before discussing molecular structure, however, we shall briefly describe the present-day conceptions of atomic structure, an understanding of which will be of use to us later on.

CHAPTER TWO

The Electronic Structure of Atoms

1. Description and Classification of Atomic Wave Functions.
Let us first consider the case of hydrogen because it is the
simplest. Given a nuclear charge of $+e$, an electronic charge
of $-e$, and the distance between them r, the potential is equal
to $-e^2/r$. The Schrödinger equation is therefore:

$$\Delta\psi + \frac{8\pi^2 m}{h^2}\left(E + \frac{e^2}{r}\right)\psi = 0$$

Solution of this equation gives the permissible energies of
the electron, which are represented by the relationship

$$E_n = -\frac{2\pi^2 m e^4}{n^2 h^2}$$

in which the number n, which is called *the principal quantum
number*, must be an integer and positive. For n 1 we obtain
the fundamental state of the atom, and with higher numbers
we obtain the various states of excitation.

For each eigenvalue of the energy (for each value of n)
there is a corresponding eigenfunction (an *orbital*), which
defines the spatial distribution of the electron. These eigenfunctions depend on, in addition to the principal quantum
number, a second quantum number l, called the *azimuthal
quantum number*, which defines the form of the spatial distribution of the electron.

For a given value of n, l may possess n integral values
0, 1, 2, ... $n - 1$. For $l = 0$ the corresponding atomic
orbitals represent a spherical distribution
of the electron about the nucleus. The
probability of the presence of the electron
varies with its distance from the nucleus but
maintains a constant value on the surface
of the sphere whose center is the nucleus.

Figure 1 is a schematic representation of
this type of orbital, which is called an *s*
orbital. There are 1*s*, 2*s*, 3*s*, etc., orbitals,

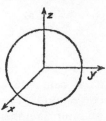

Fig. 1

9

all of which possess the same general form (spherical). They differ in their dimensions and in the effect of *the radial distribution function* (defined by $D(r) = 4\pi^2 r^2 \psi^2 dr$), which indicates the probability of the presence of the electron as a function of the distance from the nucleus (Figure 2).

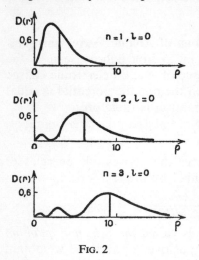

FIG. 2

In the case of hydrogen the orbitals $2s$, $3s$, etc., are only occupied in states of excitation, but in other atoms that are polyelectronic they may be already occupied in the fundamental state, as we shall see later.

Figure 3 is a schematic diagram of the form of the atomic orbital corresponding to $l = 1$, which is called the p *orbital*. An orbital of this type is represented by two equal spherical volumes tangent at the origin (the wave function has a different sign in each of the two regions); it no longer possesses spherical symmetry about the nucleus. There may also be three equivalent p orbitals

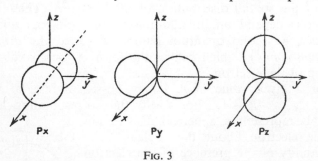

FIG. 3

oriented with respect to the three axes of a trihedron, the three axes being designated as p_x, p_y and p_z. This subdivision corresponds to a third quantum number m (the magnetic quantum number) which, for every value of l, can possess the $2l + 1$ values $0, \pm 1, \pm 2, \ldots, \pm l$. The p orbitals with the lowest energy correspond to $n = 2$ and are designated as $2p$ orbitals.

Figure 4 represents schematically the form of the orbitals corresponding to $l = 2$, known as d orbitals; the form of the orbitals corresponding to $l = 3$, known as f orbitals, is even more complex.

For a given value of n there are five d orbitals and seven f orbitals equivalent and oriented in the localized area. The d orbitals with the lowest energy correspond to $n = 3$ and the f orbitals with the lowest energy correspond to $n = 4$.

Table I summarizes the classifications of atomic wave functions up to $n = 4$. It will be observed that all of the functions corresponding to the same values of n form an electron shell. The next to last column of the table shows the number of

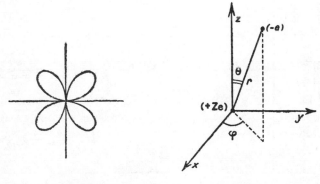

FIG. 4   FIG. 5

electrons that can be contained in each state and each shell, a problem that will be discussed in the next section. The last column shows by way of example the analytic form of the corresponding wave function expressed by means of the spherical coordinates for the orbitals $1s$, $2s$ and $2p$ of hydrogen.[1]

The case of atoms other than hydrogen is naturally more complex. Nevertheless, the previous results retain a good part of their validity. In the simplest approximation used for studying polyelectronic atoms, called the *hydrogen approximation*, the method of proceeding is very similar to that used

[1] Figure 5 illustrates the relation of the spherical coordinates to the Cartesian coordinates.

TABLE I

Shell	n	l	m_l	State	Designation	Max. No. of Electrons	Wave Function in the H atom $\left(a = \dfrac{h^2}{4\pi^2 m e^2}\right)$
K	1	0	0	s	1s	2	$\psi_{100} = \dfrac{1}{\sqrt{\pi a^3}}\, e^{-r/a}$
L	2	0	0	s	2s	2	$\psi_{200} = \dfrac{1}{4\sqrt{2\pi a^3}}\left(2 - \dfrac{r}{a}\right) e^{-r/(2a)}$
		1	0	p	2p	6	$\psi_{210} = \dfrac{1}{4\sqrt{2\pi a^3}}\dfrac{r}{a}\, e^{-r/(2a)} \cos\theta$
		1	±1				$\left\{\begin{array}{l}\psi_{211} = \dfrac{1}{4\sqrt{2\pi a^3}}\dfrac{r}{a}\, e^{-r/(2a)} \sin\theta \cos\varphi \\[2mm] \psi_{211} = \dfrac{1}{4\sqrt{2\pi a^3}}\dfrac{r}{a}\, e^{-r/(2a)} \sin\theta \sin\varphi\end{array}\right.$
M	3	0	0	s	3s	2	
		1	0, ±1	p	3p	6	
		2	0, ±1, ±2	d	3d	10	
N	4	0	0	s	4s	2	
		1	0, ±1	p	4p	6	
		2	0, ±1, ±2	d	4d	10	
		3	0, ±1, ±2, ±3	f	4f	14	

for hydrogen itself.   Here all the electrons are considered equivalent, and the spatial distribution of each one is studied in relation to the supposedly fixed nucleus while the inter-action of the electrons is disregarded.   For an atom of Z electrons and, consequently, an atomic number of Z, the problem is that of an electron with a charge $-e$, subjected to a nuclear charge $+Ze$, with the action of a central field deriving from the potential

$$V = -\frac{Ze^2}{r}$$

in which r represents the distance between the electron studied and the nucleus.   The problem is, therefore, strictly analogous to that of a hydrogen atom with a quantity close to Z in the expression of the potential energy.   In more exact calculations, which are, however, all based on the same principle, it is possible to introduce the effect of the other electrons by assuming that they exert a *screening effect* between the nucleus and the electron being studied, which reduces the effect of the nuclear field on the electron.   For an element with an atomic number Z, the field, while still considered completely central, is considered the result of a nuclear charge $Z'e$, which is smaller than Ze and is called the *effective charge*.   The *screen constants*, as they are called, for the different elements can be determined by rules that are primarily due to the work of Slater.

In polyelectronic atoms the electrons then occupy atomic orbitals which, in their general form, are completely analogous to those we have described for hydrogen.   Nevertheless, it is apparent that the orbitals of one category, the $1s$ orbitals for example, of different atoms will not have the same spatial dimensions.   Generally speaking, the more complex the atom, the closer the internal orbits to the nucleus.   Table II, which gives the radii of the atomic orbitals of various light atoms, illustrates this phenomenon.

Also the energies of the same orbitals are likewise different in different atoms.   Nevertheless, their relative values seem to maintain a nearly constant order for all elements.   In polyelectronic atoms this order, however, differs in two characteristics from that observed previously for hydrogen:

a) The orbitals with the same principal quantum numbers no longer have the same energies;

b) In the higher shells there is a partial inversion of the order of the energies between certain states of neighboring shells.

TABLE II

RADII OF SOME ATOMIC ORBITALS IN ANGSTROMS (AFTER SLATER)

Element	K	L		M			N	
	$1s$	$2s$	$2p$	$3s$	$3p$	$3d$	$4s$	$4p$
H	0.53							
He	0.30							
Li	0.20	1.50						
Be	0.143	1.19						
B	0.112	0.88	0.85					
C	0.090	0.67	0.66					
N	0.080	0.56	0.53					
O	0.069	0.48	0.45					
F	0.061	0.41	0.38					
Ne	0.055	0.37	0.32					
Na	0.050	0.32	0.28	1.55				
S	0.035	0.21	0.18	0.78	0.82			
K	0.029	0.18	0.145	0.60	0.63		2.20	
Fe	0.021	0.127	0.101	0.39	0.39	0.39	1.22	
As	0.016	0.097	0.073	0.29	0.29	0.25	0.84	1.01

In polyelectronic atoms the general order of the energies of the atomic orbitals is actually the following:

$$1s < 2s < 2p < 3s < 3p < 3d \approx 4s < 4p <$$
$$< 4d \approx 5s < 5p < 6s < 5d < 6p \approx 4f <$$
$$< 7s < 6d < 5f$$

2. The Periodic System of the Elements. In order to understand the effective distribution of the electrons in atoms and in order to explain the well-known periodicity of their properties, we must first describe three complementary properties of electrons.

1) In addition to the three previously mentioned quantum numbers, each electron is characterized by a fourth quantum number called the *quantum number of spin* and written m_s; it derives from the fact that this corpuscle behaves as if it possesses a rotational movement about its own axis, which gives rise to a characteristic rotational moment called *spin*. The quantum number of spin can have only two possible values, equal to $\pm\frac{1}{2}$ in the appropriate units.

2) *Two electrons in the same system can never have four identical quantum numbers.* This important theorem is known as *Pauli's exclusion principle.* The essential consequence of this principle is that two electrons having three identical quantum numbers n, l and m_l must have different quantum numbers of spin. An atomic orbital can therefore contain only two electrons and then only on condition that they possess what is called *opposite* or *antiparallel* spin. These electrons are said to be *coupled*.

3) In the presence of several free equivalent orbitals, the electrons always distribute themselves in such a manner as to occupy the greatest number possible; moreover, two electrons occupying singly two equivalent orbitals have *parallel spin*. This means that when an atom possesses three $2p$ electrons (as in the case of nitrogen, see below) each of these electrons occupies one of the orbitals $2p_x$, $2p_y$ and $2p_z$ and all have the same spin. These theorems are known as *Hund's rules.*

With this group of conceptions we are in a position to describe the electronic states of all atoms. To do this it is sufficient to know the number of electrons in each atom and the permissible orbitals. Each orbital is filled in succession with the electrons available, beginning with the orbitals of the lowest energy in accordance with Pauli's principle and Hund's rules. Several simple examples will provide a better explanation.

Hydrogen has only one electron, which must therefore occupy the $1s$ orbital in the fundamental state of the atom. The next element, helium, has two electrons, both of which are located in the $1s$ orbital and possess opposite spin. In the lithium atom two electrons occupy the $1s$ orbital and the third occupies a $2s$ orbital. The carbon atom, which has six electrons, has two electrons in a $1s$ orbital (with opposite spin), two others in a $2s$ orbital (opposite spin) and two others in $2p$ orbitals; according to Hund's rules these two electrons are located in two different $2p$ orbitals and have parallel spin. Oxygen, which possesses eight electrons, has two in a $1s$ orbital, two in a $2s$ orbital, two (with opposite spin) in one of the three $2p$ orbitals, e.g. $2p_z$, one in the $2p_x$ orbital and one in the $2p_y$ orbital, the last two having parallel spin.

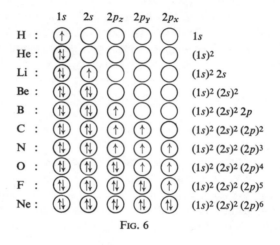

FIG. 6

Figure 6 contains a figurative description of this electron distribution; each circle represents a permissible orbital and the arrows represent the electrons within it. Opposite arrows indicate opposite spin and parallel arrows indicate parallel spin. To the right of the figure there is an abbreviated notation used to indicate the atomic state; its meaning is obvious, the index number indicating the number of electrons in the state designated in parentheses.

In this manner it is possible to estimate the maximum number of electrons that can be contained in any given electron shell. We shall leave to the reader the task of solving this problem, which may be checked by comparison with the data given in the last column of Table I. These numbers provide the key to the periodic classification of the elements. In effect, the periodicity of the properties derives from the periodicity with which the outermost electron shell of the atom (the only important one as far as the chemical and physical properties

TABLE III
PERIODIC TABLE OF THE ELEMENTS

	H	He	Li	Be	B	C	N	O	F	Ne
1s	1	2								
2s			1	2	2	2	2	2	2	2
2p					1	2	3	4	5	6

	Na	Mg	Al	Si	P	S	Cl	A
3s	1	2	2	2	2	2	2	2
3p			1	2	3	4	5	6

	K	Ca	Sc	Ti	V	Cr	Mn	Fe	Co	Ni	Cu	Zn	Ga	Ge	As	Se	Br	Kr
3d			1	2	3	5	5	6	7	8	10	10	10	10	10	10	10	10
4s	1	2	2	2	2	1	2	2	2	2	1	2	2	2	2	2	2	2
4p													1	2	3	4	5	6

	Rb	Sr	Y	Zr	Cb	Mo	Tc	Ru	Rh	Pd	Ag	Cd	In	Sn	Sb	Te	I	Xe
4d			1	2	4	5	5	7	8	10	10	10	10	10	10	10	10	10
5s	1	2	2	2	2	1	2	1	1	0	1	2	2	2	2	2	2	2
5p													1	2	3	4	5	6

	Cs	Ba	La[1]	Hf[1]	Ta	W	Re	Os	Ir	Pt	Au	Hg	Tl	Pb	Bi	Po	At	Rn
4f				14	14	14	14	14	14	14	14	14	14	14	14	14	14	14
5d			1	2	3	4	5	6	7	9	10	10	10	10	10	10	10	10
6s	1	2	2	2	2	2	2	2	2	1	1	2	2	2	2	2	2	2
6p													1	2	3	4	5	6

	Fr	Ra	Ac	Th	Pa	U
6d			1	2	3	4
7s	1	2	2	2	2	2

[1] Between La and Hf there are rare earths containing from 1 to 14 electrons of the 4f type.

are concerned) possesses the same number of electrons of the same class. Thus, for example, all alkali metals have one electron of the s type in their peripheral shell. In lithium it is a $2s$ electron, in sodium $3s$, in potassium $4s$, etc. But to pass from lithium to sodium it is necessary to fill the other half of the $2s$ orbital and the three $2p$ orbitals. Sodium consequently seems to belong in the eighth place after lithium in the periodic system. For a completely analogous reason seven elements separate potassium from sodium. On the other hand, the M shell ($n = 3$) contains, in addition to 2 electrons of the s type and 6 electrons of the p type, 10 electrons of the d type and rubidium is consequently in the 18th place after potassium, etc.

Table III gives the periodic table of the elements, up to uranium (the structure of some transuranium elements is still the subject of controversy), in which the nature of the electrons of the peripheral shell of each atom is indicated.

Two remarks should be made before conclusion of this section:

1) The progressive filling of the orbitals in the order of increasing energy corresponds to the fundamental state of the atom. These different excitational states are attained as one or more electrons are made to pass from an orbital filled in the fundamental state to one of the orbitals usually free in that state.

2) The total electronic energy of an atom, in the simplest approximation, is the sum of the energies of the filled orbitals (the orbitals occupied by two electrons are counted twice), and the total wave function is a product of the monoelectronic orbitals.

3. Hybridization of Orbitals. The pairs of electrons with different spins occupying the same orbital are no longer capable of being bound to other electrons. Consequently all evidence would seem to point to the fact that the chemical valence of an atom must be attributed only to the presence of lone electrons in the peripheral shell. According to this conception, carbon, for example, should have a valence of *two*. But it is well known that carbon in reality exhibits a valence of *four* in practically all its combinations.

To explain this phenomenon it is necessary to introduce the

important concept of *hybridization of the atomic orbitals*, which we will illustrate especially with the example of carbon because of its particular interest. In order to account for the tetravalence of carbon it is necessary to assume initially that the peripheral shell of carbon consists of four lone electrons when carbon is in its *valence state*. This occurs when one of the electrons in the $2s$ orbitals is excited sufficiently to pass over into the vacant $2p$ orbital. The energy necessary to effect this promotion of the electron can be estimated at about 90 kcal/mole. It is, however, still easy to see that this promotion itself is not sufficient to account for the experimental characteristics of carbon's tetravalence. Actually, this description provides a carbon atom possessing three equivalent orbitals oriented in mutually perpendicular directions (the p orbitals) and an orbital with spherical symmetry about the nucleus (the s orbital). This sort of arrangement would not account for the complete equivalence of the four carbon bonds in the fundamental compounds like methane, CH_4.

This difficulty was resolved by Pauling, who assumed that the orbitals that actually affect the formation of chemical bonds are not pure s, p, etc., orbitals, but mixed orbitals, *hybrids* resulting from a balanced combination of the pure atomic orbitals. The occurrence of such combinations arises from the fact that the hybrid orbitals thus obtained permit formation of stronger chemical bonds than could be obtained by the pure orbitals. This phenomenon is due to the fact that hybrid orbitals generally possess very pronounced maxima in definite directions, which allows better overlapping among them. This overlapping is responsible, as we shall see in the next chapter, for the force of the chemical bond. Thus, the energy lost in producing hybridization is compensated for by the energy gained in the formation of a stronger bond.

In the case of carbon it is assumed then that the four pure, atomic orbitals $2s$, $2p_x$, $2p_y$ and $2p_z$ can be combined to form four new hybrid orbitals defined by:

$$te_1 = a_1 s + b_1 p_x + c_1 p_y + d_1 p_z$$
$$te_2 = a_2 s + b_2 p_x + c_2 p_y + d_2 p_z$$
$$te_3 = a_3 s + b_3 p_x + c_3 p_y + d_3 p_z$$
$$te_4 = a_4 s + b_4 p_x + c_4 p_y + d_4 p_z$$

It is easy enough to determine the values of the coefficients a,b,c etc. in these equations, which, for the four orbitals sought, give the following expressions:

$$te_1 = \frac{1}{2}s + \frac{\sqrt{3}}{2}p_x$$

$$te_2 = \frac{1}{2}s - \frac{1}{2\sqrt{3}}p_x + \frac{\sqrt{2}}{\sqrt{3}}p_z$$

$$te_3 = \frac{1}{2}s - \frac{1}{2\sqrt{3}}p_x - \frac{1}{\sqrt{6}}p_z + \frac{1}{\sqrt{2}}p_y$$

$$te_4 = \frac{1}{2}s - \frac{1}{2\sqrt{3}}p_x - \frac{1}{\sqrt{6}}p_z - \frac{1}{\sqrt{2}}p_y$$

These correspond to the four equivalent orbitals of the general form shown in Figure 7, which are directed toward the four apexes of a regular tetrahedron at the center of which is the carbon atom. This type of hybridization is called *tetrahedral hybridization* and is designated by the symbol sp^3, which indicates that an s orbital has been combined with three p orbitals.

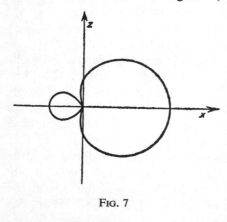

FIG. 7

Other types of hybridization are also possible in the case of carbon, and they are furthermore very important for this element and other atoms as well. The first type, which is called *trigonal hybridization*, is the combination of the s orbital and only two p orbitals (indicated as sp^2), while the remaining p orbital is left intact. In this case three equivalent hybrid orbitals are obtained, which are defined by the expressions:

$$tr_1 = \frac{1}{\sqrt{3}}s + \frac{\sqrt{2}}{\sqrt{3}}p_x$$

$$tr_2 = \frac{1}{\sqrt{3}} s - \frac{1}{\sqrt{6}} p_x + \frac{1}{\sqrt{2}} p_y$$

$$tr_3 = \frac{1}{\sqrt{3}} s - \frac{1}{\sqrt{6}} p_x - \frac{1}{\sqrt{2}} p_y$$

the geometrical form of which is analogous to that of a tetrahedral orbital, but which are this time situated in one plane
and form between them a 120° angle.   The intact p orbital,
which furnishes the fourth valence, is located in a plane perpendicular to that formed by the hybrid orbitals.

In *digonal hybridization* two p orbitals are left intact while
one s orbital is combined with only one p orbital (designated
as *sp*).   This results in two equivalent hybrid orbitals, defined
by the expressions:

$$di_1 = \frac{1}{\sqrt{2}} (s + p_x)$$

$$di_2 = \frac{1}{\sqrt{2}} (s - p_x)$$

the geometric form of which is always analogous to that of the
tetrahedral hybrid orbital but which are directed at 180° with
respect to each other; the two intact p orbitals retained by
carbon in this valence state are perpendicular to each other.
These different types of hybridization give rise to different
models of molecular structure, as we shall see in the next
chapter.

In spite of their similar form the hybrid orbitals differ from
each other both in detail and in their maximum value.   This
value decreases in the order $sp^3 > sp^2 > sp$, though all of these
have higher maximal values than the pure orbitals from which
they are formed.   If the value of a pure p orbital is 1.732, that
of an sp^3 orbital 2, an sp^2 orbital is 1.991 and an sp orbital
1.933.   Consequently, the sp^3 orbital has the most pronounced
directive character.

Hybridization of orbitals is a very widespread phenomenon
and is practically universal.   Today it is assumed that nearly
all chemical bonds are in reality formed with the aid of hybrid
orbitals.   In certain cases, however, one type of orbital very

clearly predominates, so that one may speak in a rough approximation of a bond resulting from a pure s, p, etc., orbital.

Table IV contains the main types of hybridization found in the study of chemical compounds.

TABLE IV

Type of Hybridization	Arrangement of the Hybrid Orbitals
sp	linear
dp	linear
sp^2	plane trigonal
dp^2	plane trigonal
ds^2	plane trigonal
d^2p	pyramidal trigonal
sp^3	tetrahedral
d^3s	tetrahedral
dsp^2	plane tetragonal
dsp^3	bipyramidal
d^3sp	bipyramidal
d^4s	pyramidal tetragonal
d^2sp^3	octahedral
d^4sp	trigonal prism

CHAPTER THREE

Diatomic Molecules

1. The Formation and Nature of the Chemical Bond. (The molecular orbitals method and the mesomerism method.) We are now in a position to take up the central problem of this book; the question of the manner in which quantum theory explains the existence and stability of the molecular edifice.

Let us first point out that the problem, which all evidence indicates is one of calculating the molecular energies, consists in essence of evaluating the electronic constituents of this energy.

Two principal methods have been proposed for investigating and explaining the problem that interests us: they are known as *the method of molecular orbitals* and the method of *electron pairs* or *mesomerism.* Although the mesomerism approach historically preceded the first method, we will begin with an outline of the method of molecular orbitals because it appears to be a natural extension to the molecular problem of the principles previously described with respect to the atom.

The method of molecular orbitals. The basic concept of the method of molecular orbitals lies in the assumption that an electron in a molecule can be described by a function representing its molecular orbital, just as it was possible to describe an electron in an atom by a certain function representing its atomic orbital. The difference between these two types of orbitals is that the first is monocentric, while the second must be polycentric, inasmuch as each electron is here subjected to the simultaneous effects of several nuclei. The aim of this method is first to determine the form of the orbital Ψ of each electron of the molecule and, of course, its energy. As in the case of an atom $\Psi^2 dv$ represents the probability of finding the electron in the volume dv, or in more figurative language, Ψ^2 represents the density of the electron cloud at each point in space. Also as in the case of an atom: *a*) each orbital can contain no more than two electrons with opposite spin; *b*) in the fundamental state the orbitals are filled progressively in the direction of the lower to the higher energy levels until all the available electrons have been exhausted; c) the electronic energy of the molecule in the fundamental state is, in the simplest approximation, the sum of the individual energies of the electrons; d) the corresponding wave function is the product of the monoelectronic wave function; and e) when the molecule is in a state of excitation one or more electrons pass over from one of the orbitals that are filled in the fundamental state to one or more of the orbitals that are free during that state.

Moreover, the most frequently advanced hypothesis, which today corresponds to the classical approximation of the method, consists of the assumption that *the molecular orbital of an electron can be considered as a linear combination of the atomic orbitals corresponding to this electron in the isolated atoms.* This is known as the L.C.A.O. (linear combination of atomic orbitals) approximation of the method of molecular orbitals. We shall illustrate this technique with the principal results obtained with it in the case of the particularly simple hydrogen molecule.

Let A and B be two atoms of hydrogen and let ψ_A and ψ_B be the wave functions of the electrons of atoms A and B when these atoms are separate. (These are simply the wave functions of $1s$ hydrogen electrons.) It is obvious that these functions no longer represent these electrons in the molecule, since each electron here is no longer subject to the effect of its nucleus alone but is also influenced by the other atom. Nevertheless, it is true that one can assume, strictly speaking, that when the electron is in the vicinity of nucleus A, *within the molecule,* the forces acting on it are primarily the effect of A, and its molecular orbital in that area must greatly resemble the orbital ψ_A; similarly, in the vicinity of nucleus B the orbital sought resembles ψ_B. It is therefore a natural conclusion that it is legitimate to describe the general form of the molecular orbital Ψ of an electron in the molecule H_2 by means of a linear combination of the atomic orbitals:

$$\Psi_{AB} = \psi_A + \lambda\psi_B$$

with the square of λ representing the respective contributions of the atomic orbitals to the molecular orbital.

In the case of a symmetrical diatomic molecule such as H_2 it is necessary that $\lambda^2 = 1$ and $\lambda = \pm 1$.

By writing the solution of the Schrödinger equation as applied to the problem in the form of an L.C.A.O. function one is led to the following conclusions:

1) There are two permissible electronic energy levels in this molecule. If the energy of a $1s$ electron in an isolated hydrogen atom is written as E_0, one of these levels will have an energy E_+ below E_0 and the other will have an energy E_- higher than E_0;

2) A molecular orbital

$$\Psi_+ = \psi_A + \psi_B$$

corresponds to the level E_+, while a molecular orbital

$$\Psi_- = \psi_A - \psi_B$$

corresponds to the level E_-;

3) The fundamental state of the molecule is obtained by placing the two electrons of the molecule in the orbital E_+. According to the Pauli principle these two electrons have opposite spin.

4) The orbital E_- can likewise be partially or completely filled, but the corresponding states are the excitational states of the molecule.

5) The total electronic energy of the molecule is, in the simplest approximation, the sum of the individual energies of the electrons. It is therefore equal to $2E_+$ in the fundamental state. The total wave function of the system Φ is then the product of the individual wave functions of the electrons. If the two electrons are designated as 1 and 2, the function can be written in the form

$$\Phi = \Psi_+(1)\Psi_+(2) = [\psi_A(1) + \psi_B(1)][\psi_A(2) + \psi_B(2)]$$

6) The evolution of the electronic energy of the system as a function of the distance between the bound atoms is given schematically in Figure 8 for the orbital Ψ_+ and the orbital Ψ_-. It may be observed that the curve corresponding to the orbital Ψ_+ possesses a sharply defined minimum revealing the formation of a stable compound (distance 0.85 A, energy

2.7 ev, as against the experimental values of 0.74 A and 4.7 ev, which is an encouraging agreement, given the simplified technique; this agreement can be improved by more exact

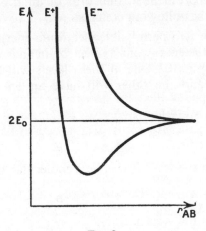

FIG. 8

methods of calculation), whereas the curve of Ψ_- shows a continuous increase of energy with increasing proximity to the nucleus, which indicates mutual repulsion existing between them.

7) The densities of the electron clouds of the orbitals Ψ'_+ and Ψ'_- are given by

$$\Psi_+^2 = \psi_A^2 + \psi_B^2 + 2\psi_A\psi_B$$
$$\Psi_-^2 = \psi_A^2 + \psi_B^2 - 2\psi_A\psi_B$$

The isodensity contours for these two states have the following general forms (Figure 9):

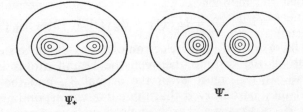

Ψ_+ Ψ_-

FIG. 9

It will be observed that for the orbital Ψ_+ *the electrons have a tendency to concentrate themselves in the region between the two nuclei, whereas for the orbital* Ψ_-*, on the other hand, they have a tendency to avoid this area.* The presence of the electrons then in the region between the two nuclei is responsible for holding the atoms together and ensures the stability of the bond. In the absence of this internuclear cement the atoms have a tendency to repel each other. This makes it easy to understand why a Ψ_+ type orbital is called a *bonding orbital* and the Ψ_- type is called an *antibonding orbital*.

The results obtained here for the particular case of the hydrogen molecule are easily generalized to fit more complex diatomic molecules.

In particular, the formation of a *simple bond* as a result of the fusion of two atomic orbitals (whether s or p) always gives rise to two molecular orbitals, one bonding and the other antibonding, of the same general type as the orbitals that we have just discussed. In homonuclear molecules these orbitals are naturally always symmetrical with respect to a plane passed through the center of the bond. This symmetry is not encountered in heteronuclear molecules for which $\lambda^2 = 1$. We will return to this important point in §3.

The type of molecular bond that we have just described is not in fact the only type that can exist between two bound atoms. The presence of multiple bonds, in particular, introduces a type of combination of atomic orbitals that exhibits certain new features. Nevertheless, the essential principles previously enumerated for the H_2 bond remain unchanged. We shall examine these additional elements and apply all of the results to obtain a more detailed description of diatomic molecules with a large number of electrons after we have described the manner in which the second great method of theoretical chemistry, the method of mesomerism, accounts for the existence of the stable chemical bonds we have just discussed.

The method of mesomerism. We shall see that the method of molecular orbitals in a formal sense divides the formation of the chemical bond into two consecutive stages: first it places the atomic nuclei in their equilibrium configuration and then studies the behavior in the field of these nuclei; this method consequently represents a point of view that considers a

molecule as composed of nuclei and electrons.[1]   The method
of mesomerism is based on a different point of view, one that
perhaps conforms more closely to the intuitions of chemists:
this method, in effect, considers all atoms as entities in
themselves and undertakes to account for the formation of
the molecular bond as a consequence of the interaction of *the
atoms* brought into contact.   We shall again illustrate the
method with the simple example of H_2, which also happens to
be the classical example since the use of the method of mesomerism to study H_2 (by Heitler and London in 1927) was the
first application of wave mechanics to the problem of the
chemical bond.

Let A and B be used again to indicate the two hydrogen
nuclei, 1 and 2 to indicate the electrons and $\psi_A(1)$ and $\psi_B(2)$,
respectively, to indicate the wave function of the electron 1
of nucleus and electron 2 of nucleus B when these two nuclei
are sufficiently far apart from each other to prevent any
significant interaction between them (these are $1s$ functions of
the hydrogen atom).   According to a fundamental theorem of
wave mechanics as applied to corpuscular systems, when the
corpuscles of such a system do not exert an influence upon
each other the total wave function of the system is the product
of the individual wave functions of the corpuscles.   In the
present case the total wave function for the system of 2 atoms
of H, *in which there is no interaction between them*, is the
product

$$\Psi_I = \psi_A(1)\,\psi_B(2)$$

What happens then if the two atoms, instead of being far
apart and without influence upon each other, are close to each
other and begin to act upon each other?   The previously
given wave function Ψ_I is certainly no longer sufficient to
describe the state of the system.   Particularly, inasmuch as
electrons are all identical and characterized by very rapid
movement, one is no longer entitled to distinguish one electron
from the other and affirm that it is electron 1 which is always
located in the vicinity of nucleus A and electron 2 that always

---

[1] In studies concerned with the valence electrons alone, which is frequently
the case with studies dealing with more complex molecules than H_2, the term
"nucleus" must be considered to include the nucleus proper and all the electrons
of the inner shells.

gravitates about nucleus B. In fact when the atoms are sufficiently close to each other one may assume that the wave function

$$\Psi_{II} = \psi_A (2) \, \psi_B (1)$$

is an equally good (or bad) description of the state of the system as was the function Ψ_I. The fundamental idea of the method of mesomerism then is the assumption that the wave function which should actually be used to describe the hydrogen *molecule* must be a linear combination of the two previously given functions:

$$\Phi = a\Psi_I + b\Psi_{II} = [\psi_A (1) \, \psi_B (2)] + c[\psi_A (2) \, \psi_B (1)]$$

Because of the molecular symmetry $c^2 = 1$, hence $c = \pm 1$.

The mathematical solution of the problem, given the previously cited hypothesis as the starting point, leads to the following principal conclusions:

1) The molecule can exist in two energy states, which are appropriately represented by

$$E_\pm = 2E^0 + E^0_\pm$$

in which E^0 represents the energy of an isolated hydrogen atom and $E^0_\pm$ the perturbational term introduced by the interaction of the two atoms. The energy E_+ corresponds to the fundamental state of the molecule, the energy E_-, to an excitational state. The curves that represent the changes of these energies as a function of internuclear distance have the same general form as the curves in Figure 8. In particular, the curve illustrating the fundamental state exhibits a minimum, which indicates the formation of a stable molecule (a distance of $0.87 \, A$ and an energy of 3.14 ev, which is in relatively satisfactory agreement with the experimental values, considering the simplified nature of the technique).

2) In the energy state E_+ the system is represented by the wave function

$$\Psi_+ = \psi_A (1) \, \psi_B (2) + \psi_A (2) \, \psi_B (1)$$

and in the energy state E_- by the wave function:

$$\Psi_- = \psi_A (1) \, \psi_B (2) - \psi_A (2) \, \psi_B (1)$$

3) The electronic density of these two states, which is obtained by calculating Ψ^2_+ and Ψ^2_-, shows that Ψ_+ corresponds to an intense concentration of the negative charge between the nuclei; and the function Ψ_-, on the other hand, corresponds to a mutual repulsion of the charges with respect to the nuclei. The stability of the molecular edifice in the fundamental state results, as in the method of molecular orbitals, from an accumulation of electrons between the bound atoms.

4) According to the Pauli principle, in the fundamental state the two electrons must have opposite spin. This is seen immediately when the principle is expressed in the following form:

The total wave function of any electronic system must be antisymmetrical (must change sign) in relation to the exchange of any two electrons. But a total wave function of an electronic system can always be represented as the product of the orbital wave function and the function of the appropriate spin. When the orbital wave function is symmetrical in relation to the exchange of two electrons, as in the case of the function Ψ_+ of H_2, it must then be multiplied by the antisymmetrical function of spin, i.e. a function of spin having the following form:

$$\delta_- = \alpha\,(1)\,\beta\,(2) - \alpha\,(2)\,\beta\,(1)$$

where, for example, $\alpha\,(1)$ indicates that electron 1 has one of the two permissible spin values, for example $+\frac{1}{2}$, in which case $\beta\,(2)$ signifies that electron 2 has a spin of $-\frac{1}{2}$, etc. The product of Ψ_+ and δ_- represents the total wave function of the system and indicates that a bond has been formed between two electrons with opposite spin.

5) We have seen that the function Ψ_+ is the sum of two products:

$$\Psi_I = \psi_A\,(1)\,\psi_B\,(2) \quad \text{and} \quad \Psi_{II} = \psi_A\,(2)\,\psi_B\,(1)$$

It is possible to provide a scheme for each of these products that would indicate the possible distribution of the electrons of the bond they symbolize. Thus, schema I in which electron 1 is in atom A and electron 2 in atom B corresponds to the product Ψ_I, while schema II in which electron 2 is in atom A and electron 1 is in atom B corresponds to product Ψ_{II}. The function Ψ_+ represents the necessity of combining the two schemas to represent the fundamental state of the electron accurately. The *exchange of electrons*, as it is called, ensures the stability of this state.

6) In order to perfect this system of representation and give it wider general significance, it is necessary to assume, in addition to schemas I and II, the interaction of schemas III and IV, in which the two electrons are both in one atom and affected by only one of the nuclei. Systems of this type

$$
\begin{array}{cccc}
1 \;\; 2 & 2 \;\; 1 & 1 \; 2 & 1 \; 2 \\
\bullet \;\; \bullet & \bullet \;\; \bullet & \bullet \; \bullet & \bullet \;\; \bullet \\
A \;\; B & A \;\; B & A \;\; B & A \;\; B \\
\text{I} & \text{II} & \text{III} & \text{IV}
\end{array}
$$

are known as *ionic formulas* (while schemas I and II are known as *covalent formulas*), and it is legitimate to suppose that they also contribute in a certain degree to the real state of the molecule. The wave functions of these two schemas can be said to correspond, respectively, to

$$\Psi_{III} = \psi_A(1)\,\psi_A(2) \quad \text{and} \quad \Psi_{IV} = \psi_B(1)\,\psi_B(2)$$

and under these conditions the wave function of the molecule can be sought in the linear combination of Ψ_I, Ψ_{II}, Ψ_{III} and Ψ_{IV}. Calculations indicate that, though the weight of the ionic formulas is no more than 4 per cent in the case of hydrogen (the two formulas naturally being present in the same proportion) their inclusion considerably improves the agreement of the theory with experience, giving a theoretical energy for the bond of about 4 ev and a length of about 0.74 A.

7) This manner of representing the actual structure of a molecule in the form of the weighted superposition of several valence schemas is the essential principle of the method of mesomerism. It should be pointed out that these valence schemas do not correspond to a tangible reality and do not describe, as is sometimes mistakenly supposed, several possible states of the molecule. Only the superposition of these schemas has a physical reality, and the only reason that we employ these simple and fictitious schemas is that we are unable to represent the actual structure of a molecule by a single formula. When the wave function of a molecule is a

linear combination of wave functions corresponding to different schemas of distribution of the valence electrons, there is said to be *resonance* (or mesomerism), which means that the molecule *resonates* between several different formulas; and this is symbolized by the sign ↔ placed between the various formulas that are capable of contributing to the actual state of the molecule. Resonance is therefore not a physical phenomenon, but represents a technique for approximating the description of molecules.

The essential results obtained for the hydrogen molecule also apply to more complex diatomic molecules. Naturally, some new elements make their appearance, for example, as a result of heteronuclear bonds or the presence of multiple bonds. The following paragraphs will be devoted to a study of these. Nevertheless, the principles that we have just enumerated for the molecular hydrogen bond are retained entirely.

Thus, the two great quantum methods placed at our disposal by wave mechanics for study of the molecule provide a satisfactory and lucid answer to the fundamental question posed in the first chapter: what is the mechanism of action of the forces producing the stability of the chemical edifice? The two methods are only two different approximation techniques for solving the same problem. They confirm the qualitative ideas of the chemists of the beginning of this century, according to which the chemical bond was attributed to the union of electrons between the bound nuclei. But the methods also determine the precise physical and mathematical sense to be attributed to the common possession of the valence electrons.

2. Description and Classification of Molecular Wave Functions. We have seen that whatever method of study was used the electron cloud forming the chemical bond in a hydrogen molecule exhibited a symmetrical distribution about the axis joining the two nuclei. In all molecules possessing a simple (single) bond a similar distribution is found, i.e. a distribution employing only two electrons, one from each atom. This distribution is characteristic of bonds formed by two electrons of the *p* type, where the directions of localization are oriented toward each other, and bonds formed by the fusion of one *s* orbital and one *p* orbital. In homonuclear molecules the cloud is moreover symmetrically divided into two parts by the plane perpendicular to the internuclear axis and equidistant from the nuclei. This second type of symmetry is naturally absent in heteronuclear molecules. This question will be examined in the following section. We will merely say here that all bonds of the type previously cited, i.e. those possessing a symmetry of revolution about the axis are called σ type bonds. There may be σs bonds and σp bonds, depending on the nature of the electrons of which they consist. Simple bonds are always of this type, and the electrons of which they are comprised are themselves frequently called σ electrons. In the method of molecular orbitals, which relates each bonding orbital to a corresponding anti-bonding orbital, there is a bonding orbital σ and an anti-bonding σ orbital, which is designated as σ^*. The bond of the hydrogen atom, which is formed by the occupation of the σ orbital by two electrons of the $1s$ type, is designated as $(\sigma 1s)^2$.

Before taking up other possible types of chemical bonds (which occur when each of two atoms possesses several free electrons and is consequently capable of forming several bonds simultaneously), it is necessary to state an important principle, which is actually the basis of all stereochemistry and known as *the principle of maximum overlapping*. According to this principle, the greater the degree of overlapping of the atomic orbitals, the greater the energy of the bond formed by them. Consequently, the bond orbitals tend to overlap as much as possible. Thus, in the case of the fluorine molecule F_2 each atom of F possesses in its outer shell two electrons of the $2s$ type and five of the $2p$ type, four of which are arranged in two doublets $2p^2_x$ and $2p^2_y$, while the $2p_z$ electron is alone. The bond is evidently formed with the aid of the two lone $2p_z$ electrons. To satisfy the principle of maximum overlapping *the coupling takes place along the z axis*, with the result that the free pairs are concentrated in the two atoms in directions perpendicular to that of the bond. The great significance of this principle will be seen most clearly in the analysis of polyatomic molecules in the next chapter, but this example should suffice to illustrate its usefulness.

Let us now consider a molecule such as O_2, consisting of two atoms each of which possesses two lone electrons, one

$2p_x$ and one $2p_y$, whose areas of localization are oriented in two perpendicular directions. One bond would be formed first by an axial overlapping of two $2p_x$ orbitals, a second, by lateral overlapping of the remaining $2p_y$ orbitals, whose directions of localization are arranged in two parallel planes after the formation of the simple bond. This new type of coupling introduces a new type of bond, the π bond. According to the method of molecular orbitals there should be a bonding π orbital and an anti-bonding π orbital (π^*). These orbitals have a completely different form from those we have been studying up to now (see Figure 10): thus, the bonding orbital

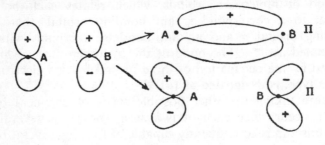

FIG. 10

is represented by two extended volumes arranged on both sides of a plane passed along the axis of the bond and perpendicular to the plane of the atomic orbitals; the wave function equals zero in the median plane and possesses different signs on either side of this. There is, consequently, no longer a symmetry of revolution about the axis of the bond. The lateral coupling that characterizes the π bond is generally less pronounced than the axial coupling of a σp bond, and therefore a πp bond is generally weaker than a σp bond.

A double bond always consists of a σ bond and a π bond. Similarly, a triple bond consists of one σ bond and two π bonds. The nitrogen molecule is an example of this. An atom of nitrogen in effect possesses three noncoupled $2p$ electrons. N_2 is therefore formed by one $\sigma 2p$ bond, produced by axial coupling of two $2p_z$ electrons, and two $\pi 2p$ bonds, produced by lateral coupling of the two $2p_y$ electrons and the two $2p_x$ electrons. The coupling that gives rise to the two π bonds occurs in two perpendicular planes. The result of this is that the overall electron distribution in N_2 takes on a symmetry of revolution about the axis of the bond.

In the description of the electron cloud, the formation and composition of which determine the molecular bond, we are only interested in the portion of the cloud arising from the combination of the orbitals possessing the lone electrons of the bound atoms. The reason for such an approach derives directly from the method of electron pairs, in which the very foundation of the bond cannot be conceived unless the atoms under consideration possess free electrons. The electron doublets consequently retain their atomic character and exert only an indirect sort of influence upon the nature of the interatomic cloud. This can also be shown to be true in the method of molecular orbitals. According to this method, once the permissible orbitals are determined they are filled progressively in the order of increasing energy by the available electrons in accordance with the Pauli principle. It can, however, also be shown that, at least in so far as the molecules formed by light atoms are concerned, the energies of the molecular orbitals are grouped in the following order:

$$\sigma 1s < \sigma^* 1s < \sigma 2s < \sigma^* 2s < \sigma 2p < \pi_y 2p$$
$$= \pi_x 2p < \pi^*_y 2p = \pi^*_x 2p < \sigma^* 2p$$

Thus, a molecule such as Li_2 should have the following configuration:

$$(\sigma 1s)^2 \, (\sigma^* 1s)^2 \, (\sigma 2s)^2$$

But when the form of the electron cloud related to a pair of orbitals such as $(\sigma 1s)^2 \, (\sigma^* 1s)^2$ is considered, it is apparent that this cloud is practically identical with that which would correspond to a simple superposition of the clouds of isolated atoms, so that it is legitimate to say that in the Li_2 molecule the electrons of the K-shell of each atom remain in the vicinity of their atom and do not take any effective part in the chemical bond. The Li_2 molecule may therefore be represented by the following notation, which symbolizes the phenomenon

$$Li_2, \, KK \, (\sigma 2s)^2$$

The preceding may be understood as follows: the superposition of each bonding orbital and the corresponding anti-bonding orbital always produces a distribution of charges that is practically the same as the simple sum of the atomic distributions. This theorem is in most cases equivalent to the exclusion of all pre-existing doublets from the effective bond. Thus, for example, the F_2 molecule may be represented by

$$F(1s^2 \, 2s^2 \, 2p^5) + F(1s^2 \, 2s^2 \, 2p^5)$$
$$\rightarrow F_1[KK \, (\sigma 2s)^2 \, (\sigma^*2s)^2 \, (\sigma 2p)^2$$
$$(\pi_y 2p)^2 \, (\pi_x 2p)^2 \, (\pi^*_y 2p)^2 \, (\pi^*_x 2p)^2]$$

The bonding character of the $\sigma 2s$ orbital and the two occupied $\pi 2p$ orbitals is neutralized by the anti-bonding effect of the σ^*2s orbital and the two occupied π^*2p orbitals, and the bond is therefore effectively the result of the pair $(\sigma 2p)^2$. Thus, it is a simple bond of the σ type.

Up to now we have been concerned only with bonds formed by the coupling of two electrons between two atoms. It might be helpful to indicate that bonds resulting from the sharing of one or three electrons between two atoms are also known. The simplest examples of these two phenomena are provided by the ions H_2^+ and He_2^+ (stable, while He_2 is not). Our theory easily accounts for the existence of these bonds. In the method of molecular orbitals they are described as follows:

$$H_2^+ : (\sigma 1s)$$
$$He_2^+ : (\sigma 1s)^2 \, (\sigma^*1s)$$

The stability of He_2^+ results from the fact that in this case the anti-bonding orbital is not more than half occupied so that it no longer entirely counterbalances the effect of the bonding orbital (as is the case in He_2, the structure of which should be $(\sigma 1s)^2 \, (\sigma^*1s)^2$).

The method of mesomerism supposes a resonance between the following forms:

$$H_2^+ \quad H. \quad H \longleftrightarrow H \quad .H$$
$$He_2^+ \quad He: \quad .He \longleftrightarrow He. \quad :He$$

3. Properties of Homonuclear and Heteronuclear Molecules. One of the characteristic properties of the distribution of the electron cloud in homonuclear diatomic molecules was symmetry about the center of the bond. This symmetry naturally disappears in heteronuclear molecules, in which the electron cloud is shifted toward one of the nuclei. Let us take as an example the formation of HCl resulting from the overlapping of the $1s$ orbital of H and the $3p_z$ orbital of Cl. The formation of the molecular orbital can be represented schematically in the following manner:

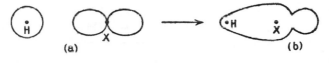

(a)   (b)

Fig. 11

The overall cloud is displaced toward the chlorine.

The two theoretical methods account for this phenomenon in different ways. The method of molecular orbitals describes the bond as the result of a molecular orbital

$$\Psi = \psi\,(1s) + \lambda\psi\,(3p_z)$$

doubly occupied, the coefficient in this case not being equal to unity. Moreover, calculations confirm that for the hydracids $\lambda^2 > 1$ so that the Ψ orbital contains more of the $3p_z$ orbital of the halogen than of the $1s$ orbital of the hydrogen. The method of mesomerism explains the phenomenon by demonstrating that of the two ionic formulas (besides the usual covalent formulas) that are a priori capable of representing HCl, H^+Cl^- and H^-Cl^+ the first has much greater preponderance, which is easy to understand, since the energy required to form the ions H^- and Cl^+ is much greater than for the ions H^+ and Cl^-. For all practical purposes we may disregard the effect of the formula H^-Cl^+ and consider only the resonance between the covalent formula and the ionic formula H^+Cl^-.

One of the essential results of this symmetry in the distribution of charges along the axis is that the molecule takes on a *permanent dipole moment* equal, by definition, to the product of the pure charge of the atoms and the distance between them. Evidently this moment increases as the coefficient λ of the molecular orbital increases in its difference from unity or as the weight of the ionic formula in resonance with the covalent formulas becomes greater. In principle, the theoretical evaluation of λ or of the weight of the ionic formula should permit the dipole moment to be predicted. In practice, however, these calculations are generally very difficult to carry out, so that frequently the operation is reversed and the experimentally calculated moment is used to determine the theoretical magnitude.

It is easily shown that:

1) In the method of molecular orbitals the relation between λ and the dipole moment μ in a first approximation has the form:

$$\mu = \frac{(\lambda^2 - 1)e\mathrm{R}}{1 + \lambda^2}$$

where R is the interatomic distance and e the charge of the electron.

2) In the method mesomerism, if the molecule is represented by $\Psi = \Psi_{cov} + \delta\Psi_{ion}$ the relation between δ and μ is given by:

$$\mu = \frac{100\delta^2 e\mathrm{R}}{1 + \delta^2}$$

the quantity $\dfrac{100\delta^2}{1 + \delta^2}$ representing "the percentage of the ionic character of the bond."

3) The polar character of a bond can be associated with a property of an element that chemists call the "electronegativity" of the element and which by definition represents the attraction exercised upon the electrons in a molecule by the element. The polar character becomes greater as the difference in the electronegativity of the bound atoms increases.

4) Several definitions that would make possible the establishment of an electronegativity scale have been proposed; the most important of these are due to the work of Mulliken and Pauling. According to Mulliken the electronegativity of an element is equal to half the sum of its ionization potential and its electronic affinity. According to Pauling, the difference between the electronegativity of the two elements A and B $(X_A - X_B)$ is given by:

$$23.06(X_A - X_B)^2 = \Delta_{AB}$$

where Δ_{AB} represents the difference between the real energy of the molecule and the energy it would possess if the bond were purely covalent (expressed kcal/mole).

TABLE V

H						
2.1						
Li	Be	B	C	N	O	F
1.0	1.5	2.0	2.5	3.0	3.5	4.0
Na	Mg	Al	Si	P	S	Cl
0.9	1.2	1.5	1.8	2.1	2.5	3.0
K			Ge	As	Se	Br
0.8			1.8	2.0	2.4	2.8
Rb						I
0.8						2.5
Cs						
0.7						

This latter hypothetical energy is obtained by assuming that the energy of a pure covalent bond A—B is equal to the arithmetic (or geometric) mean of the energies of the homopolar bonds A—A and B—B. Consequently, Δ_{AB} measures in some way the energy of the resonance between the covalent and ionic forms.

Table V contains a portion of Pauling's scale of electronegativity.

It is easily seen that with few exceptions this quantity follows a regular progression as a function of the position of the element in a column or rank of the periodic system.

Table VI contains by way of illustration the numerical values of the different magnitudes given for the hydracids.

On the whole it seems clear that wave mechanics not only provides an explanation of the reasons underlying the very existence of the molecular bond, but also makes possible a precise description of the different forms that this bond can take.

It should be pointed out that, though wave mechanics accepts the practical utility of the division of bonds into ionic and covalent bonds, it clearly recognizes that this division is purely formal and that all real bonds are intermediate between these two fictitious extremes. Some bonds may be closer to a pure covalent bond, others, to a pure ionic bond, but the difference is in reality a quantitative question.

TABLE VI

Molecule	μ (1)	R (2)	μ/eR	λ	δ	% of the ionic form
HF	1.98	0.92	0.45	1.9	0.86	45
HCl	1.03	1.28	0.17	1.3	0.45	17
HBr	0.78	1.43	0.11	1.2	0.36	11
HI	0.38	1.62	0.05	1.1	0.23	5

Molecule	Energy of the bond (3)	Δ_{AB} (4)	$X_A - X_B$	$\frac{1}{2}(I_A + E_A) - \frac{1}{2}(I_B + E_B)$ (5)
HF	147	77	1.9	258
HCl	102	22	0.9	124
HBr	83	11	0.8	90
HI	63	−7	0.4	54

(1) In Debye units ($1D = 10^{18}$ u.e.s.).
(2) In Angstroms ($1A = 10^{-8}$ cm.).
(3) In kcal/mole.
(4) Taking as the energy of the covalent bond A—B the arithmetic mean of the energies of the bond A—A and B—B, with the following experimental energies (in kcal/mole):

$$H_2 = 104, \quad F_2 = 35, \quad Cl_2 = 57, \quad Br_2 = 45 \quad \text{and} \quad I_2 = 36.$$

(5) I_A = Ionization potential of A, E_A = The electronic affinity of A, etc. (in kcal).

The methods of wave mechanics then accomplish a synthesis of the limiting conceptions of the previous periods and demonstrate the continuity of the possible forms of chemical bonds.

CHAPTER FOUR

Non-Conjugated Polyatomic Molecules

The use of the previously described quantum methods in the study of polyatomic molecules tends to divide them into two major classes, which may be designated as *non-conjugated* molecules and *conjugated* molecules. The first group of molecules includes compounds formed with simple bonds alone or compounds containing only isolated multiple bonds separated from other multiple bonds or free doublets by several simple bonds. The second group of molecules includes those compounds that contain two or more multiple bonds arising from adjacent carbon atoms or next to atoms containing free doublets.

From the point of view concerning us here, the essential difference between these two classes of molecules lies in the fact that the non-conjugated molecules can be described conconveniently in terms of the approximation known as *localized bonds*; according to this approximation the molecule is considered as a simple juxtaposition of diatomic bonds, while the conjugated molecules must be described by the more general approximation known as *non-localized bonds*, according to which the interaction among all parts of the molecule are considered to play an essential role in the properties of the bond. The characteristics of this second class of molecules will be considered in the next chapter, while the present chapter is devoted exclusively to the study of non-conjugated molecules.

1. Localized Bonds. The constancy of the properties of the bonds of non-conjugated polyatomic molecules has led to their consideration as structures resulting from the juxtaposition of localized bonds. Among these constant properties one might first cite the length of the bonds. Thus, for example, the constant value of $1.54 A$ characterizes the length of a simple C—C bond in many saturated hydrocarbons. A constant value of $1.34 A$ might be ascribed to the length of a double C=C bond in all the compounds where the bond is isolated from other multiple bonds or from atoms possessing free pairs. Fixed lengths could also be ascribed to the bonds C—H, O—H, C—halogen, N—H, etc., in all molecules falling within the category of non-conjugated molecules. Another notably constant characteristic of the bonds is their energy. Thus, for example, the total energy of a molecule such as CH_4 may be considered equal to the absolute value of the sum of the energies of the four equivalent C—H bonds. Now it has been found that the energy thus attributed to a C—H bond remains practically unchanged in all saturated hydrocarbons. This is also true for other types of bonds, so that it is possible to draw up energy tables of the determined bonds, making it possible to find the experimental energy of non-conjugated compounds by simple addition of the appropriate values. In fact, a good definition of non-conjugated molecules consists precisely of the statement that their energy is the sum of the energies of their bonds considered as localized bonds. Another characteristic of these bonds which is practically constant is their polarity. Table VII summarizes these characteristics for several important bonds:

TABLE VII

Bond	Length (in A)	Energy (in kcal)	Polarity (in D)
C—H	1.10	87	0.3
O—H	0.96	110	1.5
N—H	1.01	84	1.3
S—H	1.35	86	0.7
C—Cl	1.77	67	1.6
C—Br	1.91	54	1.5
C—N	1.47	49	0.5
C—O	1.43	70	0.9
C=O	1.24	150	2.4
C—C	1.54	59	
C=C	1.34	100	
C≡C	1.20	123	
O—O	1.47	35	
O=O	1.21	96	

It is apparent that the experimental constancy of the properties of the bonds makes it legitimate to consider the polyatomic molecules in which they occur as simple juxtapositions of several diatomic systems. Obviously in such molecules the electronic interaction is limited to the adjacent atoms alone. The overlapping of orbitals, or if one prefers, the coupling of the electrons, takes place between pairs of orbitals or electrons that are well defined, without any influence from the various coupled doublets. The formation of each bond may be considered as the result of the mechanism described in the preceding chapter, with each bond being formed independently of the others and retaining its particular properties.

We shall soon see how this conception squares with our knowledge of the spatial structure of these molecules. But even here it must be emphasized that the approximation of localized bonds is not completely satisfactory in any case. In effect, even in the simplest polyatomic molecules, the various bonds are not completely independent of each other. On the contrary, mutual interactions certainly do exist between all the atoms constituting the molecule. It is true, however, that these interactions are in comparison very slight, so that it is possible to neglect them in a first approximation, but only in a first approximation. The situation is quite different in the conjugated molecules, where it is necessary to account for these interactions even in the simplest approximation. There is, in fact, a continuous range of molecules with bonds more or less localized. We shall take this up in the paragraphs that follow the discussion of electronic delocalization in the molecules that are considered non-conjugated in a first approximation.

2. Directed Valences and Stereochemistry. The theory of directed valences combined with the principle of maximum overlapping makes possible, as we have already seen, an easy explanation of the spatial structure of simple molecules. At the same time it provides us with a precise explanation of the significance of the approximation of localized bonds.

Let us consider a triatomic molecule of the simplest type, containing a central divalent atom bound to two monovalent atoms: water, H_2O. We know that an oxygen atom possesses in its peripheral shell two lone $2p$ electrons whose directions of localization form a 90-degree angle. In conformity with the principle of maximum overlapping, which leads to the strongest bonds and therefore to the most stable molecule, the two OH-bonds (which are type σ) form along the axes of localization of the $2p$ electrons of the oxygen (see Figure 12). From this

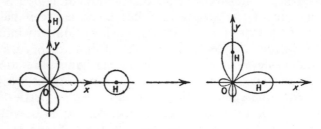

Fig. 12

it follows that in the approximation of localized bonds, i.e. bonds that are independent of each other, the angle between the two OH-bonds should be 90 degrees. This angle is experimentally determined at 104 degrees, a result sufficiently close to theory for us to consider the approximation of localized bonds satisfactory, but too far from theory for us to consider this approximation perfect. The experimentally encountered augmentation of the angle may be attributed to two principal factors: a) the existence of a coulomb repulsion between the two OH-bonds as a result of the polarity of these bonds, according to which the hydrogen atoms possess an excess positive charge; b) the oxygen valences are not pure p valences, but actually hybrid valences resulting from a slight hybridization between the $2p$ and $2s$ electrons of that element.

These factors of induction and hybridization are actually encountered in all analogous examples and represent the principal causes of the discrepancy between the experimental observations and the hypothesis of localized bonds. Nevertheless, it is certain that from a practical point of view the most convenient method of studying non-conjugated molecules is to assume the approximation of localized bonds and if necessary the intervention of secondary effects.

Several other important examples of the principal spatial configurations of non-conjugated molecules are given in the following paragraphs:

a) NH_3: the nitrogen atom possesses three lone $2p$ electrons, and the molecule is formed, according to the principle of maximum overlapping, in the shape of a triangular pyramid (Figure 13). The experimentally determined valence angle H—N—H is again enlarged to 107 degrees.

b) BCl_3: the boron atom has one $2s$ doublet and one lone $2p$ electron in its outer shell. Hybridization among the three electrons gives three valences of the sp^2 type. The molecule lies in one plane, and the angle of the valences is 120 degrees (Figure 14).

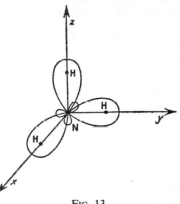

FIG. 13

c) CH_4 (methane): the carbon is in the sp^3 state, and the molecule has the form of a regular tetrahedron with the carbon at the center (Figure 15). The angle of the valences is 109 degrees 28 minutes.

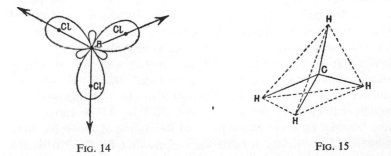

FIG. 14   FIG. 15

d) C_2H_4 (ethylene): the two carbons are in the sp^2 state. The hybrid valences are used to form one C—C bond and four C—H bonds. The angles C—C—H and H—C—H are about 120 degrees. All the bonds are of the σ type. The pure p valences of the carbon form by lateral coupling a second C—C bond which is of the π type (Figure 16). As the overlapping of the p orbitals is at a maximum when these orbitals are parallel, the formation of the π bond imposes a coplanarity on all the atoms composing the molecule, the π electrons themselves being in a plane perpendicular to that formed by the atoms. This makes possible a *cis-trans* isomerism in the disubstituted derivatives (at the two carbon atoms) of ethylene.

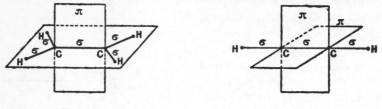

FIG. 16   FIG. 17

e) C_2H_2 (acetylene): the two carbon atoms are in the *sp* state. The hybrid valences form the two C—H bonds and an initial C—C bond of the σ type, the atomic group being collinear. The four remaining $2p$ electrons form two π bonds located in two perpendicular planes (Figure 17). Free rotation about the C—C axis is therefore possible.

3. The Flexibility of the Molecular Model. The geometric arrangements that we have just described represent the usual models for simple molecules, but naturally do not constitute rigid models that require no modification for the different possible derivatives of the previously described compounds. It is apparent, for example, that in a methane derivative where one of the hydrogens has been replaced by a halogen the valence angles and the characteristics of the remaining C—H bonds will be different from those of CH_4. The most convenient way of accounting for this flexibility of the molecular model and providing for the variations that this will produce in the properties of the localized bonds is to express the phenomenon as a function of the modification of the state of hybridization of the bound atoms and above all the polyvalent atom. Thus, a useful and quite general rule provides that when an atom is substituted with another atom of greater electronegativity, e.g. when a halogen is substituted for one of the hydrogens of methane, there is an increase in the proportion of the *p* orbital in the bond established with the substituent. Naturally, the proportion of the *s* orbital increases in the bonds directed toward the other atoms or the remaining hydrogen atoms in our example. (Obviously the reverse should occur during substitution with a less electronegative element.) The principal consequences of this change are the following:

a) a decrease in the valence angle H—C—halogen (which is in effect equal to 93 degrees in CH_3Cl);

b) an increase in the angle H—C—H (which is in effect equal to 118 degrees in CH_3Cl);

c) a shortening of the C—H bonds (which are in effect equal to 1.05 A in CH_3Cl).

One particular reason for the deformation of the theoretical model may sometimes be the effect of internal tensions. In effect, in all the examples considered up to now the establishment of the bonds was regulated by the principle of maximum overlapping, one of the consequences of which is that in the formation of simple bonds the engaged orbitals point directly toward each other. The bonds are, so to speak, rectilinear. Nevertheless, it is conceivable that in certain cases a mechanism of this sort may encounter resistance arising from the necessity for too great a deformation of the valence angles. Let us consider, for example, the case of a molecule such as cyclopropane

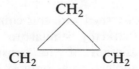

The carbon atoms which, in principle, are all in the sp^3 valence state, which corresponds to a normal valence angle of 109 degrees 28 minutes, are situated at the apexes of an equilateral triangle. It is evident that if the overlapping of the orbitals forming the C—C bonds here takes place along the line joining these carbons the molecule will undergo great internal tensions. It is conceivable then that a more favorable energy arrangement could be obtained if the orbitals forming the C—C bonds were directed in such a manner as to form a certain angle with the axis joining the carbons: the reduction of the overlapping would be compensated for by a reduction in the internal tensions. Calculations indicate that the most stable model for cyclopropane corresponds, in effect, to the existence of a 22-degree angle between the direction in which the orbitals of the C—C bonds point and the C—C axis. These C—C bonds may therefore be considered as curved bonds. The deformation of the valence angles is naturally connected to a modification of the hybridization state, which is no longer a perfect sp^3 state, but an intermediate state that is closer to sp^2.

4. Hydrogenated Substances with an Electron Deficit. "Bridge" Structures. Hydrogenated substances with a deficit of electrons, i.e. substances possessing less valence electrons than the amount necessary to form by coupling the whole group of interatomic bonds, make up a special group of molecules to which it is impossible simply to apply the notions developed up to here. The problem deserves special examination.

The classic example of these compounds with an electron deficit is that of diborane B_2H_6. In fact, if the existence of a boron hydride BH_3 is disregarded, diborane is a stable compound that does not dissociate at even 100 degrees C. Now this compound has only 12 valence electrons, a quantity that is just enough to unite the six hydrogen atoms to the boron atoms by the usual covalent bonds, but this leaves no electron for the boron-boron bond.

The first theory concerned with this compound assumed that the structure was markedly similar to that of ethane and proposed the formulation of the substance as $BH_3 \cdot BH_3$. Since, however, the molecule has only 12 valence electrons for seven bonds, it was assumed at the same time that in contrast with ethane, where each bond is formed by the coupling of two electrons, diborane contained only twelve-sevenths electrons for each bond. To account for this state of affairs it was assumed that the molecule resonated between a certain number of formulas which possessed a bond of one electron between the boron and the hydrogen, for example:

$$
\begin{array}{ccc}
\text{H} & & \text{H} \\
.. & & .. \\
\text{H} . \text{B} & : & \text{B} . \text{H} \\
.. & & .. \\
\text{H} & & \text{H}
\end{array}
$$

in which we have indicated all the valence electrons for greater clarity. We will recall that a one-electron bond exists effectively in the H_2^+ ion, so that it would not be a priori impossible in other circumstances.

Nevertheless, a whole body of experimental data, particularly spectroscopic data, has led to the abandonment of this model and to the adoption of a very special structure for diborane, called "bridge" structure and indicated schematically as:

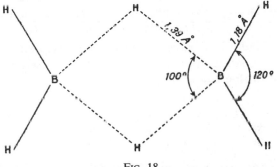

FIG. 18

In this structure the two terminal BH_2 groups are coplanar and the two central hydrogens are arranged symmetrically above and below this plane. We have also indicated in the figure the geometric dimensions proposed for this model. In addition to allowing us to interpret satisfactorily the different spectroscopic properties of diborane, this model is also in agreement with the purely chemical data which distinguish effectively the two types of hydrogen by means of substitution reactions: only four of the six hydrogen atoms of this compound can be substituted.

The bridge structure, though explaining the spatial configuration of the molecule, does not tell us much about the very nature of the bonds assuring the stability of such an edifice. At first one might be tempted to suppose that we have here encountered a particular type of bond, known as the "hydrogen bond," which is quite frequently met with and which consists of a union of two atoms by the intermediation of a hydrogen atom placed between them.

It is, however, easily seen that this cannot be the case.

Actually the difference between the electronegativities of boron and hydrogen is almost nil, so that the conditions necessary for establishing the strong electrostatic interactions that are indispensable for the "hydrogen bond" are completely absent in this compound. In reality the internal structure of the "bridge" bond is not yet completely clear. It is certain, however, that because of the insufficiency in the number of valence electrons one must assume their delocalization to account for the formation of all the necessary bonds. Among the various suggestions concerning the internal structure of the "bridge" bond, two especially should be retained:

a) Diborane would have a constitution essentially similar to ethylene except that two protons would be inserted into the π bond according to the schema:

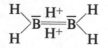

b) The bridge should be constructed of two identical tri-atomic bonds formed by a combination of two approximately tetrahedral hybrid orbitals belonging to the two boron atoms with the $1s$ orbital of the appropriate hydrogen. The form of these bonds should be the following:

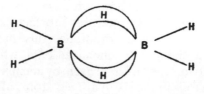

FIG. 19

On the whole the problem of the structure of bridge type bonds is not yet completely resolved and further studies are required.

Diborane is only one of many boron compounds possessing bonds with bridge structure. There are other boranes such as B_4H_{10}, B_5H_9, B_5H_{11}, B_6H_{10}, etc., that pose the same problem.

Moreover, the bridge type bond is not peculiar to boron compounds alone and is also encountered in hydrogen derivatives of other elements. We will cite in particular the interesting case of aluminum hydride, where each aluminum

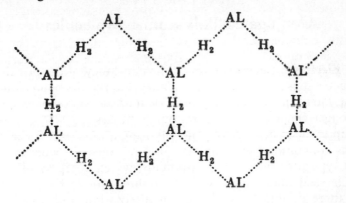

atom is surrounded by six hydrogens, the overall group being capable of forming an infinite polymer according to the above schema.

Gallium and beryllium also exhibit this type of bond, for example, in the compounds

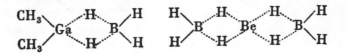

CHAPTER FIVE

Conjugated Polyatomic Molecules

1. Electronic Delocalization. The constancy of the principal characteristics (length, energy, polarity, etc.) of the bonds found in the molecules which have been defined as non-conjugated is no longer encountered in compounds possessing two or more multiple bonds arising from neighboring atoms or adjacent to atoms containing free doublets. Let us consider benzene, the most typical of the cyclic compounds, which is represented by the classical notation as formed of three simple C—C bonds and three double C=C bonds in alternation and six C—H bonds. If such a formula were capable of representing the structure of this substance in a satisfactory manner

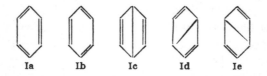

Ia   Ib   Ic   Id   Ie

the properties of this substance would consist of a simple juxtaposition of the properties of these various bonds: the carbon-carbon distances would alternate between 1.54 A (the length of the C—C bond) and 1.34 A (the length of the C=C bond); the energy of the molecule would be equal, in absolute value, to the sum of the energies of the three C—C bonds (3 × 59 kcal/mole), three C=C bonds (3 × 100 kcal/mole) and six C—H bonds (6 × 87 kcal/mole), i.e. 999 kcal/mole. However, experimentally all the carbon-carbon bonds of benzene are equivalent and they all have a length of 1.39 A, which lies between the characteristic lengths of the simple carbon-carbon bond and the double carbon-carbon bond; moreover, the empirical energy of the molecule as deduced, for example, from the combustion heat is about equal to 1.039 kcal/mole. The real molecule is therefore some 40 kcals more stable than the hypothetical molecule described by formula Ia or Ib. The approximation of localized bonds is then, in this particular case, completely inadequate. The situation is the same for all other conjugated molecules.

It is not difficult to understand why the localized bond approximation is inadequate to explain a molecule such as benzene. We saw, in effect, in the preceding chapter that the principal condition, the fulfillment of which is necessary for the validity of this approximation, is the existence at the heart of the molecule of pairs of orbitals (of electrons) belonging to neighboring atoms, that overlap (couple) to a considerable extent in the absence of any appreciable overlapping (coupling) with other orbitals (electrons) present in the molecule. It is easy to see that this condition is not fulfilled in a case such as that of benzene. The six carbons forming the hexagonal skeleton of this molecule are, from all evidence, in the sp^2 state of hybridization. From this it may be inferred that the three hybrid orbitals of each carbon are used to form a C—H bond and two C—C bonds with the neighboring atoms, all these bonds being of the σ type and forming the rigid skeleton of the simple bonds of the molecule. Each carbon then still possesses a pure $2p$ orbital pointing in a direction perpendicular to that of the three σ bonds and capable of forming a π type bond by means of lateral overlapping with the analogous orbital of the neighboring carbon. As this overlapping

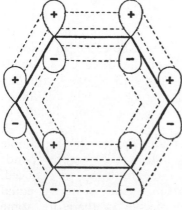

FIG. 20

is at a maximum when these orbitals are parallel, for all the carbon atoms they will tend to point in the same direction perpendicular to the plane formed by the skeleton of the simple bonds. Under these conditions, it is immediately apparent that each one of the pure $2p$ orbitals has an equally good chance of combining with the neighbor on its left as with the neighbor on the right and that it is, therefore, not legitimate to assume an exclusive coupling with one of these neighbors (Figure 20). From this it follows that:

1) All the carbon-carbon bonds of benzene are equivalent;

2) There are no simple C—C bonds or double C=C bonds of the type encountered in non-conjugated molecules, but bonds of a new type intermediate between these extremes, a type of simple C—C bond that is endowed with some of the characteristics of the double bond. This conclusion is already in agreement with the intermediate length of these bonds.

Consequently, we shall distinguish in the case of benzene, and in a general manner in all conjugated molecules, two groups of electrons, which may be described by two different approximations: the group of σ electrons forming the rigid skeleton of simple bonds, which are localized bonds, and the group of π electrons forming an electron cloud divided about the skeleton and representing delocalized or mobile bonds. As the probability of the presence of any π electrons in the plane formed by the skeleton of σ electrons is null, the two groups may be considered separately. Furthermore, it is the π electrons, which are held more loosely than the σ electrons, that are practically responsible for all the properties peculiar to conjugated molecules. Consequently, it is to these electrons that studies are generally limited, the inclusion of the σ electrons simply representing a shift of origin in the scale of magnitudes studied.

Let us now see how the great theoretical methods approach the description of these "delocalized bonds." In both cases the technique employed, which is different in each method, essentially represents an extension to a polyatomic problem of the theory established for diatomic molecules. For both we shall use the example of benzene.

The method of molecular orbitals describes each π electron of the molecule by means of a molecular orbital extended to all the carbons. If these carbons are numbered 1 to 6 and if the atomic orbitals in the vicinity of the carbons 1, 2, etc., are designated as ψ_1, ψ_2, etc., the L.C.A.O. approximation, the most usual approximation of this method, gives the molecular orbital of each electron, Ψ_i as a linear combination of these atomic orbitals:

$$\Psi_i = c_1\psi_1 + c_2\psi_2 + \cdots c_6\psi_6$$

The squares of the coefficients c_1, c_2, etc., define the probability of finding the electron under consideration at one of the various carbons 1, 2, etc.   There are as many molecular orbitals as there are π electrons, and in the fundamental state of the molecule the lowest orbitals are occupied successively until all the available electrons are exhausted in electron pairs with antiparallel spin.   In benzene there are therefore six molecular orbitals, three of which are occupied in the fundamental state.

The method of mesomerism deals with the delocalized bonds by assuming that the molecule cannot be satisfactorily described by a single formula that represents a well-determined distribution of the electrons of the multiple bonds (such as the Ia formula for benzene), and that it is necessary to use several formulas simultaneously.   One therefore says that the molecule *resonates* between these different valence schemas, which simply means that the real structure lies between the structures symbolized by the different formulas and can only be represented by a weighted superposition of these.   Also, it is assumed that benzene resonates between at least formulas Ia and Ib, since these two formulas taken together represent the fact that each π electron has an equal chance of coupling with its left or right neighbor.   In reality it is generally assumed that the resonance of benzene is not limited to these two formulas (called the Kekulé formulas), but that it also consists of the three formulas with remote bonds (called the Dewar formulas), which represent the possibility of coupling between electrons located in non-neighboring atoms.   The wave function Ψ of the molecule is then considered as a linear combination of the wave functions ψ_a, ψ_b, ..., ψ_e, corresponding to each of these formulas:

$$\Psi = a_1 \psi_a + a_2 \psi_b + \cdots a_5 \psi_e$$

The squares of the coefficients a_1, a_2, ..., a_5 represent the "weights" of these formulas in the representation of the real molecule.

In certain very recent, more perfect calculations the interaction of the ionic formulas is also taken into consideration.

Electronic delocalization is characteristic of all molecules possessing multiple bonds abutting on adjacent atoms or possessing free doublets located at atoms adjacent to an atom with a multiple bond.   The following are examples of several simple conjugated molecules; in each case the principal formulas between which they are assumed to resonate are given:

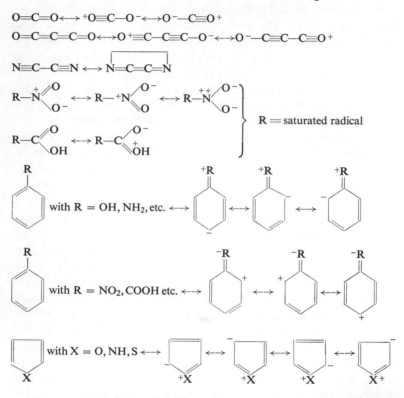

2. The Energic and Structural Indices and Their Significance.

A more precise study of the various manifestations of electronic delocalization leads to the definition of a number of energic and structural indices that can be quantitatively determined and that describe the various characteristics of conjugated molecules. Naturally some of these indices apply as well to non-conjugated molecules, and frequently their values in this class of compounds constitute points of reference for a study of the consequences of delocalization.

The indices defined by the two methods have, in general, an analogous significance, although their mathematical expressions and their numerical values may be different. Some of these indices, however, are peculiar to one of the two methods. Let us first consider the indices of the method of mesomerism, which are more susceptible of a simple figurative representation.

In this method the calculations provide directly the energy of the molecule in its fundamental state and in the various excitational states when necessary. The energy thus obtained is different from the hypothetical energy that would be obtained for the molecule with the use of the approximation of localized bonds, i.e. by supposing that it could be correctly described by a single formula. The difference between the real energy of a molecule and the hypothetical energy it would possess if it were represented by one of the classic formulas is called the *resonance energy*, and as reference one takes the formula that is apparently the most stable. Thus, the resonance energy of benzene is given by the difference between the real energy, calculated by assuming a resonance between several valence schemas, and the energy of a Kekulé formula alone. The resonance energy is always positive, which means that the existence of a resonance always represents an increase in stability. The resonance energy (in kcal/mole) of several typical compounds is: 36 for benzene, 77 for naphthalene, 152 for pyrene, 3.6 for butadiene, 24 for pyrrole, 29 for thiophene, 16 for benzoquinone, 33 for CO_2, etc. It is a very important quantity in the study of chemical equilibriums.

The difference in energy between the fundamental state and the various excitational states, which can be called the *transition energy*, is of interest in spectroscopy: it defines the position of the corresponding absorption bands according to the formula:

$$\nu = \frac{\Delta E}{hc}$$

where ν is the frequency of the light emitted, ΔE the transition energy, h the Planck constant and c the speed of light. In particular the difference in energy between the fundamental state and the first excitation state gives the frequency of the absorption band closest to the visible.

The method also introduces two important structural magnitudes:

1) The *mobile bond index*. In the different formulas that contribute to the structure of benzene a given bond is sometimes represented as a double bond and sometimes as a simple bond.

The sum of the weights of all the formulas that represent this bond as double is called the *mobile index* of a bond. Thus, for example, the calculations for benzene show that the weight of each Kekulé formula is 0.390 and the weight of each Dewar formula is 0.073. Each benzene bond is represented as double in a Kekulé formula and in a Dewar formula, and its mobile index is equal to 0.390 plus 0.073, which equals 0.463. According to this conception the index of a simple C—C bond, as in ethane, is 0, and that of a double C=C bond, as in ethylene, is 1.

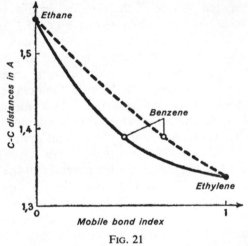

FIG. 21

This conception of the index of a bond is very useful, inasmuch as many properties of bonds appear to develop in a regular fashion as functions of the mobile index. Among the properties that should be cited, the first is bond length.

Standard curves can be drawn for various types of bonds (for example, for the carbon-carbon bond) using as reference points the data for particularly important compounds (ethane, benzene and ethylene); curves of this sort make possible the calculation of the length of any intermediate bond if its index is known. Figure 21 provides such a curve for the carbon-carbon bond, the broken line representing the same curve as calculated from the method of molecular orbitals. The concept of a bond index is also important in interpretations of chemical reactivity (for details see the next section).

2) The *free valence index*. The remote bonds figuring in the Dewar formulas for benzene represent the coupling of π electrons situated in non-adjacent atoms. It is legitimate to assume that this coupling must be very weak and that it can easily be transformed into a "free valence." The free valence index of an atom is defined as the sum of the weights of all the formulas in which a remote bond abuts on this atom. For a carbon atom in benzene this index is therefore equal to 0.073. An equivalent definition takes the free valence index of an atom as the difference between a constant (which is equal to unity in this method) and the sum of the indices of the bonds taking their origin from this atom (see further on the definition ascribed to this magnitude in the method of molecular orbitals). For benzene the free valence index is: $1 - 2 \times 0.463$, equal to 0.073. The notion of free valence is of greatest importance in accounting for the reactivity of the various atoms of a molecule (see also the following section).

Let us now consider the manner in which the method of molecular orbitals defines the same magnitudes.

a) *Resonance energy*. This is the difference between the real energy of the molecule, obtained by taking into account the delocalization of the π electrons and the energy that would be ascribed to the molecule by the approximation of localized bonds. In this method the magnitude might be more appropriately called the energy of delocalization.

b) *Excitational energies*. These are always equal to the difference between the excited state of the molecule and the energy of its fundamental state; they provide the position of the absorption bands. The different excitational states occur when one or more electrons pass from an occupied orbital to an unoccupied orbital. In particular, the first excitational state arises when an electron is passed from the highest occupied orbital to the lowest free orbital. The corresponding excitational energy defines the position of the absorption band closest to the visible.

c) *Bond and free valence indices*. In the method of mesomerism these two indices depended on the coefficients representing the various contributions of the different formulas to the real structure of the molecule. In the method of molecular orbitals they are expressed as a function of the coefficients representing the contributions of the atomic orbitals to the molecular orbitals. Thus, the contribution of a π electron situated in a given orbital to a bond between the two atoms r and s can be considered as the product of the coefficients $c_r c_s$ of this orbital. Thus, the index of the bond between these two atoms can be considered as the sum of the $c_r c_s$ extended to all the orbitals occupied in the fundamental state (the orbitals occupied by 2 electrons are counted twice).

The free valence index of an atom is defined on the basis of the bond indices. Let us consider the sum of the mobile indices of the bonds abutting on the atom r, and let us suppose that the value of this sum is known for all the compounds containing atoms of this element, e.g. carbon; let C be the greatest of these values. In some fashion C represents the highest capacity of carbon to form π bonds. When for any carbon in a given molecule the sum of the indices of the bonds adjacent to this carbon is lower than C, one may say that the capacity of this carbon to form π bonds is not completely utilized and that the carbon possesses a certain "free valence" that could be measured by the difference between C and this sum. It is convenient to take C as equal to 1.732 in the method of molecular orbitals in order to keep the free valence index positive.

Calculations indicate that in this method the bond index in benzene is equal to 0.667 and the free valence index of carbon in this molecule is 0.398.

d) The *electric charge index*. It is also possible to define an index of the mobile electric charge, which would measure the total quantity of π electrons situated around each atom. For an atom r this magnitude is given by the sum of c^2_r, taken for all the orbitals occupied in the fundamental state (the orbitals occupied by two electrons are counted twice). This index is very important in determining the dipole moments of the molecules and also, like the other structural indices, in problems of chemical reactivity. (We might mention that an analogous index of charge can be defined in the method of mesomerism, but because of the difficulty of the calculations in accounting for the ionic formulas it is of little importance.)

The method of molecular orbitals is also very useful, and in practice much more so than the method of mesomerism, for the study of several other physical magnitudes, particularly those magnitudes involving individual electrons:

Molecular ionization potentials. It can be shown that the ionization potential of an electron is equal in absolute value in a very good approximation, to the energy of the molecular orbital in which it is located: best known is the first ionization potential, equal to the energy of the highest occupied orbital.

Molecular reduction potentials. It can also be shown that the polarographic reduction potential of hydrocarbons is equal in absolute value, with the exception of a constant, to the energy of the lowest free orbital that will be occupied by the electrons responsible for the reduction.

Diamagnetic anisotropy. Conjugated molecules are characterized experimentally by a diamagnetic anisotropy. Calculation of this magnitude is not easy. It can be shown that in the method of molecular orbitals, which is better suited for these calculations, the anisotropy is equal to the sum, extended to all of the occupied orbitals (an orbital occupied by two electrons is counted twice), of the second derivative of the magnetic field of the energies of the orbitals.

3. Aromatic Molecules and Their Peculiar Properties. It is in the aromatic molecules that the various manifestations of electronic delocalization are most clearly seen. We will now examine this class of compounds to illustrate the significance of the previously defined magnitudes.

We shall not concern ourselves here with the ionization and molecular reduction potentials (the study of which is not as yet much developed) or with diamagnetic anisotropy (the study of which is difficult); as for the other properties, we shall make use of the indices of either method without distinction, as they are of practically equal value.

1) *Resonance energy.* We have already mentioned that in addition to furnishing information concerning the stability of different types of molecules this magnitude is of particular importance in the study of chemical equilibriums. Let us consider for example the formation of free triphenylmethyl radicals resulting from the homolytic dissociation of hexaphenylethane according to the schema:

$$\begin{array}{ccc}
\text{Ph} \diagdown \quad \diagup \text{Ph} & & \diagup \text{Ph} \\
\text{Ph}-\text{C}-\text{C}-\text{Ph} & \rightarrow \quad 2 \quad \bullet\text{C}-\text{Ph} \\
\text{Ph} \diagup \quad \diagdown \text{Ph} & & \diagdown \text{Ph}
\end{array}$$

The ease with which this dissociation takes place (the energy of this dissociation is only 11 kcal/mole, while the energy of the dissociation of hexamethylethane is 80 kcal/mole) and the stability of the free radicals formed was for a long time an enigma. Today that ease of dissociation is known to be due, to a great extent, to increased possibilities of resonance available to the free radical. In fact, the resonance energy of hexaphenylethane is practically equal to six times that of an isolated benzene. The sum of the resonance energies of two triphenylmethyl radicals is higher than this quantity because of a supplementary resonance resulting from the delocalization of the lone electron in accordance with the possibilities:

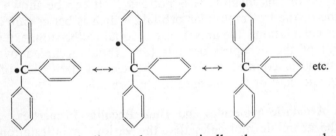

Calculations indicate that practically there are only 0.2 electrons at the "trivalent" carbon atom, the rest being scattered among the phenyls, and that the complementary resonance energy acquired as a result of this delocalization is of the order of 20 kcal/mole for each free radical. The resonance then contributes 40 kcal/mole to the reduction in the dissociation energy; the remaining 30 kcal/mole are provided by the mutual repulsion of the phenyls, which tends to weaken the medium C—C bond.

A related problem is posed by the existence of biradicals, compounds possessing two uncoupled electrons with parallel spin. A simple rule that can be used to determine substances of this sort before they are found in this state is that these are the molecules for which no Kekulé formula can be written. An example of such a substance is Schlenk's hydrocarbon:

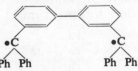

The stabilization of these molecules is due in this case also to the possibility of delocalization of the free electrons over the overall contour.

2) *Transition energies.* The most significant of these energies for chemists is the one with the lowest numerical value, because it determines the position of the absorption band closest to the visible (λ_{max}.) and is consequently responsible for such color as the molecules may have. Precise calculations in this area have provided information that has made possible an understanding of the observed phenomena such as could hardly be obtained otherwise. This is why experimental chemists frequently have a tendency to content themselves with merely connecting the different spectroscopic properties of molecules with certain other structural properties characteristic of their fundamental state. Although such correlations are often useful, they unfortunately do not go to the heart of the matter; only the calculation of the transition energies can explain the actual nature of these phenomena. Quantum theory has already had considerable success in this area. First, it has been found possible to predict correctly the position of λ_{max}. in different types of conjugated molecules (see Table VIII), if an appropriate value is chosen for some of the relevant intervening parameters. The calculations establish the fact that the existence of electronic delocalization displaces the overall group toward the visible, but these calculations are also capable of accounting for many more delicate observations.

TABLE VIII

Molecule	λ max. obs. (in A)	λ max. calc. (in A) (method of mesomerism)
Butadiene	2,100	1,900
Hexatriene	2,600	2,570
Benzene	2,600	2,470
Naphthalene	2,750	2,680
Styrolene	2,850	2,570
Biphenyl	2,515	2,570
Fulvene	3,650	3,650
Azulene	7,000	6,910

It can, for example, be seen from Table VIII that the calculations very clearly indicate the differences in the position of λ_{max}. in pairs of isomers such as benzene and fulvene (II) or naphthalene (III) and azulene (IV). However, while the presence of delocalized bonds always produces a displacement of the spectra in the direction of the longer waves as compared to a hypothetical model with localized bonds, an increase in the number of conjugated multiple bonds does not always necessarily increase this displacement. Thus, a bathochromatic effect of λ_{max}. is observed in passing from benzene to naphthalene and a hypsochromatic effect is observed in passing from fulvene to benzofulvene. It has been one of the recent

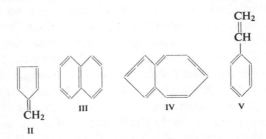

successes of the theory to account easily for such differences in behavior. The theory, at least in its simple form, is confronted with many difficulties in correct evaluation of the intensity of the transitions and their polarization direction.

3) *The electric charges.* The distribution of these makes possible the determination of the dipole moment of the molecules. Among the great recent successes of the theory in the area of aromatic compounds one might cite the conjecture according to which: a) the electric charges (of the π electrons) should be uniformly equal to unity in all the carbons of hydrocarbons formed of benzene rings and heterocyclic double bonds; b) the electric charges should differ from unity in conjugated hydrocarbons containing a cycle with an uneven number of sides (e.g. fulvene or azulene). The molecules of the former group should then have no dipole moment, whereas the latter group should possess a dipole moment (because they do not have symmetry that would be opposed to this). This conjecture has been thoroughly confirmed by experience, styrolene (V), for example, possessing practically no dipole

moment, while fulvene has a dipole moment of 1D. The numerical agreement between theoretical and experimental values is not excellent in the classical approximation, but more exact calculation gives a very close to complete agreement. This is a result that the qualitative conceptions would be completely incapable of predicting or even interpreting.

Moreover, the conjugated molecules apparently constitute, because of the mobility of their assemblage of electrons, a fluid medium where a perturbation of the charges at any point has immediate repercussions over the whole aggregate of the periphery; and, in effect, the theory has had much success in predicting the perturbations produced in the charge distribution of a hydrocarbon by the attachment of a substituent or the introduction of a heteroatom. Thus, for example, one can easily find by calculation the preferential activation of the *ortho* and *para* positions of benzene when a substituent possessing a free doublet and capable of entering into resonance with the electrons of the multiple bonds of the molecule is introduced. (If the qualitative representation of the theory of resonance is considered, this is explained as resulting from the greater significance of the formulas activating the previously cited vertices than the formulas essentially activating the *meta* vertices, these latter necessarily exhibiting, in addition to the separation of the charges, a remote bond (see Figure 22).)

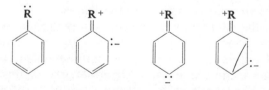

FIG. 22

We shall see further on, in relation to the carcinogenic capacity of aromatic compounds, an interesting application of such calculations to the larger molecules.

The distribution of electric charges naturally also plays a great part in chemical reactivity. The major portion of the reagents is made up of negative or positive ions, and it is natural to suppose that they attack preferentially the positive or negative centers of a molecule. It must be remembered, however, that the distribution of electric charges that we have just considered is characteristic of the isolated molecule in the absence of any exterior disturbance.   But the approach of the reagent modifies this distribution or, as one says, *polarizes* the molecule, so that it is the distribution of charges in this transition state that determines the evolution of the reaction, and not the initial distribution.   It is possible, and it frequently happens, that there is, in fact, a parallelism between the characteristics of the initial state and of the transition state, so that an examination of the initial diagram often allows the course of the chemical reaction to be predicted.   But for a rigorous understanding, new indices, which could be called *dynamic* in contrast with the *static* indices of the molecules in the normal state, should be defined to describe the properties of reacting molecules.   The most important of these indices are the *polarization energies*, which represent the energies necessary to deform the electronic structure of a conjugated molecule sufficiently to favor maximally the proposed reaction.   Let us take, for example, the case of naphthalene attacked by a positive ion.   It is assumed that the easier it is to localize a whole negative charge (a supplementary π electron) at one of the carbon atoms of the molecule, the easier it is for the reaction to take place. Now the energy necessary to produce such a deformation can be calculated by assuming that this localization can take place either at an α carbon or a β carbon.   The less energy required for this deformation, the easier the reaction.   The calculations indicate that the energy of such a polarization is several kcal/mole less for an α carbon than for a β carbon.   Consequently, it is at an α carbon that the reaction must take place, as in effect it does.   A particularly interesting fact is that the calculations indicate that substitution of naphthalene with a negative ion should also take place at the α carbon, because this carbon is also more easily polarized for this reaction than the β carbon.   This prediction is also verified by experience.   In a general fashion, it has been confirmed that in all the usual aromatic hydrocarbons that do not possess an uneven ring structure and in which the charges are equal to unity in all the carbons, all the substitution reactions have a tendency to take place at the same carbon atom (see the following section).

4) *The bond and free valence indices.* One of the principal applications of the bond index is in predicting the interatomic distances. See, for example, the results of the calculations for the different bonds of naphthalene as compared to very recent results of an x-ray analysis of the same molecule (Table IX). The overall agreement is very satisfactory, and this is also true for almost all the known cases.

TABLE IX

Bonds	Bond index		Calculated distances		Observed Distances
	Method of M.O.	Method of mesom.	Method of M.O.	Method of mesom.	(in A)
A	0.725	0.557	1.37	1.37	1.36
B	0.555	0.347	1.41	1.42	1.42
C	0.603	0.367	1.41	1.41	1.40
D	0.518	0.255	1.43	1.44	1.40

B A
D C

Generally speaking, all the bonds of a conjugated system are partially multiple, since the "simple" bonds acquire a certain mobility index and are therefore shortened in length in the saturated molecules, while the "double" bonds lose a portion of their mobility index and undergo an elongation. From the experimental point of view, this phenomenon can have curious stereochemical consequences. Thus, in the conjugated polyenes, e.g. butadiene $CH_2\!=\!CH\!-\!CH\!=\!CH_2$, the conjugation of the double bonds confers a considerable mobile index (or double bond character) on the "simple" median bond; in fact, this index is 0.447 by the method of molecular orbitals. The result is that the molecule loses the possibility of rotating freely about this central bond, which it would have if this were really a simple bond. Experimental information, particularly spectroscopic data, indicates the existence of two isomers of butadiene, differing in the spatial arrangement of the double bonds in relation to the central bond: the isomers are called *s-cis* and *s-trans* (to distinguish them from the usual isomers relating to a double bond, which could be called *d-cis* and *d-trans*):

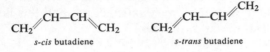

s-cis butadiene   s-trans butadiene

These two isomers are in thermal equilibrium, with the *s-trans* isomer predominant at normal temperature.

Conversely, in certain particular compounds the "double" bonds may undergo so pronounced a diminution of their mobile index that they actually lose the character of double bonds and no longer give rise to the usual *cis-trans* isomerism or give rise to it very weakly. This is the case with compounds of the type of dibiphenyleneethylene (VI), in which the otherwise easily interconvertible stereo-isomers are rarely encountered. The central bond index of dibiphenyleneethylene is only

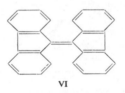

VI

0.673 (by the method of molecular orbitals). It may be noted that in the classic formula this bond is in the immediate vicinity of four other double bonds, whereas it is not usual for a double bond to neighbor on more than two other multiple bonds.

A further application of the bond index is related to chemical reactivity. It has indeed been found that for many addition reactions that occur at adjacent vertices (e.g. ozonization), the greater the mobile bond index between these vertices, the easier it is for the reaction to take place. For example, in the case of naphthalene the α-β bond is preferred to the β-β bond for these reactions; similarly, the 9–10 bond of phenanthrene, which possesses a particularly high mobile index (0.775 by the method of molecular orbitals), is particularly suitable for these additions. For greater rigor it would be appropriate here also to replace the static indices with dynamic indices, but in practice the

parallelism between these two groups of indices is very satisfactory in the majority of the known cases.

The principal application of the *free valence index* is also
related to chemical reactivity. In the first place, the value of
this index directly determines the capacity of a vertex to react
on radical substitution. In the second place, it has been found
that in practice, at least among the aromatic hydrocarbons that
do not contain uneven rings, the polarizability of a carbon for
ionic substitutions generally varies directly with its free valence
index. This is the reason why all these substitutions have a
tendency to occur, as we have seen in the previous section, at
the same carbon atom, e.g. the α-vertex of naphthalene.

5) *The carcinogenic activity of aromatic hydrocarbons.* As a
rather unusual example of the usefulness of the methods of
quantum analysis of electronic delocalization we will briefly
consider the important problem of the carcinogenic properties
of the aromatic hydrocarbons.[1] Today it is indeed almost
possible to declare with certainty that this activity is connected
with the presence of electronic delocalization: with several
rare exceptions, this activity is exhibited only by molecules with
conjugated double bonds, and it can always be suppressed by
suppression of the conjugation, e.g. by hydrogenation of the
system.

Moreover, this activity is extremely sensitive to the slightest
modifications in the electronic structure of the molecules
capable of provoking it. Thus, for example, benzanthracene

VII

(VII), a compound from which the greatest number of carcinogenic compounds derive, is itself inactive. Nevertheless,

[1] For an account of recent developments and an overall treatment of the
subject (without mathematical details), see A. Pullman and B. Pullman, *Can-
cérisation par les substances chimiques et structure moléculaire*, Masson, Paris,
1955.

the introduction of a disturbing element as slight as a methyl group can, depending on the site at which it is introduced, produce compounds that are also inactive (substitution at 8), compounds that are weakly active (substitution at 6 or 7), compounds that are noticeably active (substitution at 5 or 9) and even compounds that are very active (substitution at 10). It is quite evident that the usual conceptions of chemists can only with great difficulty explain, and hardly at that, the gradation of properties resulting from a simple change in the position of the substituent. Quantum methods achieve this explanation without much difficulty.

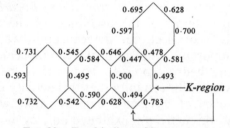

FIG. 23. Bond indices of benzanthracene

In effect, general considerations of the mode of activity of carcinogenic hydrocarbons suggest that the first stage of this activity must consist of the formation of a complex between the cellular element that is the site of the carcinoma and the active molecule. Examination of the distribution of the structural indices of benzanthracene, and particularly of the distribution of its bond indices (the electrical charges of all the carbon atoms being equal to unity) indicates that such an addition would occur preferentially at the 3–4 bond, which is the most "double" in this molecule (it is called the K-region, see Figure 23).

Starting from this hypothesis, it is not difficult to determine (at least in principle, because the actual calculations are complicated by the size of the molecule) by one of the quantum methods described in this work in what fashion the presence of a methyl at various carbon atoms of the molecular periphery would modify the capacity of the K-region to react to form the complex. Since the methyl group belongs to that class of substituents that is capable of effecting a transfer of charges in this hydrocarbon, it may be concluded that a supplementary accumulation of charges produced in that region by the presence of methyl groups in the molecule produces an increase in the reactivity of the K-region. It has in fact been found that this accumulation runs parallel with the carcinogenic activity. Thus, the increase in the charge of the K-region produced by attachment of methyl to benzanthracene is 0.008 e for a substitution at 8, 0.011 e for a substitution at 6 or 7, 0.015 e for a substitution at 5 or 9 and 0.023 for a substitution at 10. This parallelism is also encountered in the polymethyl derivatives of benzanthracene and in the alkyl derivatives of other aromatic carcinogenic hydrocarbons. Let us single out a further obvious example: it has been found that the methyl derivatives

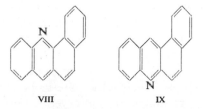

VIII   IX

of benzo-1,2-acridine (VIII) are much more carcinogenic than the derivatives related to benzo-3,4-acridine (IX). This phenomenon is easily explained by theory: in contrast with methyl groups, a nitrogen atom placed in an aromatic ring lowers the carbon charge at the periphery; and calculations indicate that the charge reduction in the K-region is greater in benzo-3,4-acridine than in the 1,2-isomer. Consequently, the methyl derivatives of the first of these compounds has a K-region with a lower charge than the analogous derivatives (with the nearer position of the nitrogen) of the second isomer, which explains within the scope of the theory we have just described why there is a difference in the degree of carcinogenic activity of the two compounds.

There is no doubt that the purely qualitative methods could not have explained a problem so delicate or complex as this. It should be mentioned that a series of experimental studies resulting from these theoretical investigations appears to confirm the importance of the K-region in carcinomas resulting from aromatic hydrocarbons.

4. Resonance and Planarity. Before concluding this chapter one important fact should be emphasized: complete manifestation of the effects connected with electronic delocalization requires planarity of the molecule. This condition is in fact indispensable, as we saw at the beginning of this chapter, for the existence of any appreciable overlapping among the $2p$ orbitals situated in parallel planes. If, for any reason (steric obstructions, internal tensions, etc.), this planarity is destroyed, one observes a partial or total disappearance, depending on the degree of destruction, of the characteristics resulting from the conjugation. One of the most sensitive indications of a defect (even slight) in the planarity of the conjugated system is given by spectroscopic observations. Let us consider, for example, the particularly well understood case of the substituted derivatives of biphenyl (X). Though the biphenyl molecule is probably not planar in a rigorous sense, a considerable conjugation occurs between the two rings and gives rise to a characteristic spectrum for biphenyl. When substituents are attached in the *meta* or *para* positions, only the normal spectroscopic effects which are to be expected from the nature of these groupings are observed. On the other hand, the presence of *ortho* substituents effects a complete change in the spectrum. Thus, the spectrum for dimesityl (XI) more closely resembles that of mesitylene (XII) than that of biphenyl: the presence of four *ortho* methyls no longer permits the molecule to retain a planar structure, not even approximately, and results in a marked rotation of the two benzene rings in relation to each other.

Other sensitive indications of the destruction of planarity are given by the interatomic distances and the dipole moments.

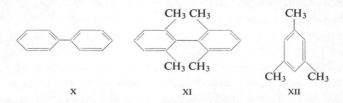

CH₃ CH₃   CH₃

CH₃ CH₃   CH₃   CH₃

X   XI   XII

CHAPTER SIX
The Structure of Complexes

The first method of representing the double salts, complex compounds resulting from the union of two saturated molecules, consisted of dualistic formulations such as those proposed by the electrostatic theory of Berzelius for all chemical substances. Thus, for example, the complex compound that is today called potassium ferrocyanide was written $4KCN \cdot FeCN_2$. It soon became obvious, however, that this notation was completely inadequate: in the first place, it could be shown that in solution this compound dissociates into ions and that one of these ions is made up of the group $[Fe(CN)_6]^{4-}$, which must therefore represent an entity at the very center of the complex, and, in the second place, it was hardly possible to differentiate chemically, using the dualistic formula, the CN groups bound to the potassium from those bound to the iron.

The first theory of the structure of complexes was put forward by Werner (1905) and, though the primitive studies of this author were of course perfected, his general conception was retained. According to Werner's theory, double salts are formed by the association of complex ions, such as the previously cited $[Fe(CN)_6]^{4-}$, with simple ions, such as the four K^+ ions in potassium ferrocyanide. The two parts of this edifice are held together by electrostatic attraction between the charges of opposite sign. The complex molecule should be written $[Fe(CN)_6]K_4$.

The important problem of the internal structure of the complex ion, however, remains to be solved. Werner postulated that this ion was formed by the binding of the central atom to the accompanying groups by means of bonds analogous to those introduced into organic chemistry by Dumas and his school and today called covalent bonds. This idea, which the future was to confirm, was not, however, easy to explain at that time. Indeed, this conception implied that in the ferrocyanide ion the central iron was bound to six CN groups according to the scheme:

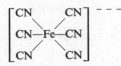

The valence of the iron in this ion was thus higher than usual for iron, which was 2 or 3. Werner then proposed to distinguish two sorts of bonds within the complex ion, the ones determined by the usual valence of the central atom, its principal valence, and the ones determined by an additional valence, which was in some sense secondary and which was only encountered in these particular complexes. This idea had to be abandoned because there were no experimental indications that distinguished between two different types of bonds in the interior of the complex ion. In fact, the important problem of the internal structure of this ion could not be solved, as we shall see in a moment, without the quantum theory.

Nevertheless, another of Werner's observations has continued to retain its importance to this day: the knowledge that in a series of related complex ions possessing the same central atom, the total number of atoms or groups bound to this central atom remains constant. The nature of these groups may, of course, vary considerably. Consider, for example, some of the iron complexes in which the central atom is associated with groups of completely different character:

$$[Fe(CN)_6]K_4; \quad [Fe(H_2O)_6](NH_4SO_4)_2;$$
$$[Fe(CN)_5NH_3]Na_3;$$
$$[Fe(NO_2)_6]K_2Ca; \quad [FeF_6](NH_4)_3$$

In all these cases, however, the total number of groups bound to the central iron atom is six. This constant has been given the name of *coordination index* or of *coordination number*, and it represents one of the most important characteristics of complexes. In a great number of complexes and for many elements this number is equal to either 6 or 4.

Now let us consider how these empirically obtained facts are interpreted by the modern theory. The first observation that is useful in this area is that the atoms that give rise to complex ions belong, in general, to the groups of transition elements which contain d-electrons in the shell nearest to their peripheral shell. Let us consider as examples the metals iron, cobalt and nickel, which are particularly important in the formation of complexes, and let us divide their electrons into two groups:

a) an interior group formed, in the case of these three elements, by the complete K and L shells, the two electrons of the $3s$ type and the six $3p$ electrons, the aggregate forming the electronic configuration of argon; and

b) an outer group formed of a certain number of $3d$ electrons (6 in the case of iron, 7 in cobalt and 8 in nickel) and a $4s$ doublet. Only the outer group is important in the problem now under consideration. The $3d$ state, which possesses five degenerated orbitals, may contain up to 10 electrons. When the number of available electrons is less than this, they are distributed according to Hund's law, which was given in Chapter Two. The electronic structure of the outer group of Fe, Co and Ni, in the fundamental state of these elements, can then be represented in the following manner (Table X):

TABLE X

Element	3d					4s	4p			No. of uncoupled electrons
Fe	↑↓	↑	↑	↑	↑	↑↓				4
Co	↑↓	↑↓	↑	↑	↑	↑↓				3
Ni	↑↓	↑↓	↑↓	↑	↑	↑↓				2

Moreover, the energy differences between the $4s$ and $4p$ states and even $3d$ and $4p$ are relatively slight, frequently of the order of several tens of kcals. Consequently, electron jumps between these orbitals are possible and the previously cited elements can exist in multiple valence states. Thus, for example, the atom Fe can exist not only in the valence state $(3d)^6 (4s)^2$ indicated, but also in a state $(3d)^6 (4s) (4p)$ or $(3d)^5 (4s) (4p)^2$. In conformity with Hund's rule it has six and eight lone electrons, respectively, in the last two states.

The same phenomenon is also encountered in the different ions derived from these atoms. Thus, for example, in its fundamental state the Fe^{4-} ion (an atom of iron with four captured electrons) should in principle have the structure $(3d)^{10} (4s)^2$; all the $3d$ orbitals would then be doubly occupied and there would be no lone electron. In fact, this ion primarily exists in a valence state with the structure $(3d)^8 (4s) (4p)^3$: one of the $4s$ electrons and two of the $3d$ electrons are passed to the $4p$ orbitals. In this valence state the ion Fe^{4-} has six lone electrons: two $3d$ electrons, one $4s$ electron and three $4p$ electrons. Table XI gives by way of example the valence states of iron and its different ions:

TABLE XI

Atom	Valence state	No. of free electrons
Fe	d^6s^2	4
	d^6sp	6
	d^5sp^2	8
Fe $^+$	d^6s	5
	d^5s^2	5
	d^5sp	7
Fe^{2+}	d^6	4
	d^5s	6
Fe^{3+}	d^5	5
Fe $^-$	d^5sp^3	9
Fe^{2-}	d^6sp^3	8
Fe^{3-}	d^7sp^3	7
Fe^{4-}	d^8sp^3	6

Since the ion Fe^{4-} has six valence electrons, it is capable of forming six covalent bonds with other atoms or groups. However, if all this took place, for example, in carbon compounds, these bonds would not actually be effected by means of pure $3d$, $4s$ or $4p$ orbitals, but with hybrid orbitals composed of these simple orbitals. The cause underlying this hybridization again resides in the possibility of forming by this means six new orbitals pointing in well-determined directions and possessing a very high maximum. In fact, the orbitals resulting from hybridization of the $4s$ electron, three $4p$ electrons and two $3d$ electrons (a hybridization written as sp^3d^2) are among the most frequently encountered in the chemistry of complexes: this is octahedral hybridization, the six equivalent hybrid bonds being directed toward the six apexes of a regular octahedron (Figure 24). Their maximum is 2.923.

Not only does this explain the fact that the central atom of the complex ion $[Fe(CN)_6]^{4-}$ can form six equivalent covalent bonds of the σ type with the six surrounding groups, but it also predicts the spatial distribution of the bonds. Experience effectively confirms the octahedral structure of a great number of complexes for which this structure was predicted by the theory. In particular, this geometric configuration is encountered in numerous classic complexes of cobalt.

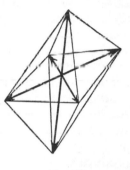

Fig. 24

A second mode of hybridization that is also relatively widespread among complex ions of certain elements is the type sp^2d, which is known as tetragonal hybridization. It possesses four equivalent orbitals, with a maximum equal to 2.694, that are situated in a single plane and enclose 90-degree angles. This is the case, to mention only the classical examples of the ion complexes of nickel, with the $[Ni(CN)_4]^{2-}$ ion or with the platinum ion $[PtCl_4]^{2-}$. The corresponding valence states containing the necessary number of lone electrons again result from electronic excitation between the states $3d$ or $4s$ and $4p$. (In relation to this point it may be worth mentioning that one must not conclude from the preceding that all the tetra-coordinated complexes of nickel necessarily correspond to a tetragonal hybridization: nickel carbonyl $Ni(CO)_4$ is a classic example of a tetrahedral hybridization.)

The brief description of the structure of complex ions that we have just given, though a correct representation of their geometrical configuration and a satisfactory rendering in modern terms of the concept of coordination, is only a first approximation of the description of the nature of the bonds binding the central atom to the surrounding groups. Up to now we have represented these bonds as simple covalent bonds of the σ type.   In fact, their electronic structure is more subtle. In the first place, we should note that if the simple representation was satisfactory it would lead us to attribute a very high distinct electrical charge to the central atom. The ion $[Fe(CN)_6]^{4-}$, for example, would have to be written:

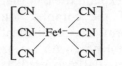

Such an arrangement is very improbable. Present conceptions tend to adopt a postulate *of neutrality* to represent the real electronic distribution in these complex ions; this postulate suggests that an internal rearrangement of electrons occurs here that tends to even out the excess distinct charges and produce a more homogeneous distribution. This evening out can be obtained in two principal ways. In the first place, when the atoms that are directly bound to the central atom have an electronegativity distinctly different from the latter, the covalent bonds between these atoms acquire a certain ionic character that becomes more pronounced as the difference in the electronegativity becomes greater; this contributes to the diminution of the distinct charge of the central atom.

This phenomenon occurs to a certain degree in the ion $[Fe(CN)_6]^{4-}$, though the difference of electronegativity between the iron and the carbon is not very great: the electronegativity of iron is 1.7, that of carbon 2.5. The difference of 0.8 corresponds to an approximately 10 per cent ionic character for the bond C—Fe. In reality this value is probably higher because the great reduction in the charge of the carbon effected by the nitrogen should increase the tendency of the carbon to decrease in its turn the charge of the iron atom.

The second factor contributing to the evening out of the distinct charges and to their concentration at the periphery of the ion complex rather than at the central atom lies in the possibility of the formation of multiple bonds between the central atom and the surrounding groups. Such bonds involve the *d* electrons present at the central atom and not involved in the formation of the simple bonds. It may be noted in the table that the iron atom can exist in the valence state

(d^5sp^2), in which it is capable of forming eight covalent bonds. When this atom acquires an electron and is transformed into the ion Fe^-, it possesses nine lone electrons and is then capable of forming nine covalent bonds. Nine is the maximum number of covalent bonds that the transition elements can form in their different valence states. The ion Fe^{2-} has only eight free electrons. The valence 7 is found for the ions Fe^{3-} and Fe^+ and the valence 6 for the ions Fe^{4-} and Fe^{2+}. In reality, however, it must be assumed that the different types of formulas in which the central iron acquires certain valence states contribute equally to the real structure of the complex ion. This is particularly so for the following formulas in which the central atom is respectively nonavalent, octavalent, heptavalent and hexavalent (each of the designated formulas naturally corresponds to a group of analogous formulas that it can be deduced from by making use of the symmetry of the complex ion).

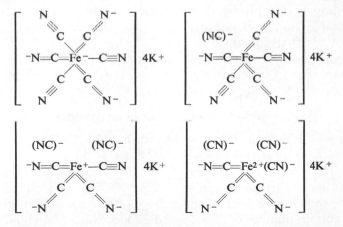

It is found that as a consequence of the resonance between these different formulas, the bonds between the iron and the six CN groups surrounding it are partially ionic, partially σ and partially π. The π bonds are formed with d electrons that do not participate in the hybrid σ bonds.

Thus, for example, in the first of the formulas cited the ion Fe^- is in the valence state d^5sp^3; it therefore possesses nine free electrons. Six of these electrons take part in the formation of six hybrid orbitals sp^3d^2. There are then three free d

electrons that form the double bonds, which are of the π type. For obvious reasons of symmetry the six bonds between the central atom and the surrounding groups are naturally identical. One of the consequences of the partially double character of these bonds is the transfer of the charge formally belonging to the iron to the nitrogen atoms situated at the periphery of the complex ion.

It is important to emphasize that in many cases the partially double character of the bonds existing in octahedral or tetragonal complexes has been used as experimental evidence in the measurement of interatomic distances: these bonds have proved to be shorter than the corresponding simple hybrid bonds.

It is hardly possible to conclude this short chapter on the structure of complexes without adding a word on the magnetic properties of this group of substances. In effect, these properties constitute an important characteristic, frequently aiding in the precise determination of the ionic structure of complex ions. It is generally known that the chemical compounds that contain only coupled electrons are diamagnetic, while those possessing one or more free electrons are paramagnetic. Quantitatively, the resultant of the moments of spin of n lone electrons is equal to:

$$\mu = \sqrt{n(n + 2)} \quad \text{Bohr magnetons}$$

or $\mu = 1.73$ for $n = 1$, $\mu = 2.83$ for $n = 2$, $\mu = 3.88$ for $n = 3$, $\mu = 4.90$ for $n = 4$ and $\mu = 5.92$ for $n = 5$.

The simple compounds of the transition elements are for the most part paramagnetic. This is easily understood since the monatomic ions of these compounds contain, in general, a certain number of noncoupled $3d$ electrons, and Hund's rule requires that when a layer is not completely filled the electrons tend to occupy the maximum available compartments. Thus, for example, the distribution of the outer electrons of the iron atom being $(3d)^6 (4s)^2$ this element contains four $3d$ electrons that are not coupled. The usual simple ions derived from this, Fe^{++}, and Fe^{+++}, have the structure $(3d)^6$ and $(3d)^5$. They therefore contain four and five lone electrons respectively. Experimental measurements confirm this, these ions possessing effectively a magnetic moment of 5.3 and 5.9 Bohr magnetons.

It is easy to guess all of the advantages offered by a quantitative characteristic of this type in the determination of the structure of complex ions of these same elements.

In effect, if such ions continue to be paramagnetic, it means that there are a certain number of lone $3d$ electrons in them (the number can be determined by the value of the moment); if, on the other hand, these ions are diamagnetic, it means that all the evidence indicates that they do not possess any more free electrons and that, consequently, the latter have all been coupled during the formation of the coordination bonds. Thus, for example, experimental determination of the fact that the complex $[Fe(CN)_6]K_4$ is diamagnetic confirms our representation of it, according to which all the free electrons are engaged in the formation of simple or double bonds. On the other hand, it is observed that the complex $[Fe(CN)_6]K_3$ is paramagnetic, the experimental value of its moment indicating the presence of a free electron.

This complex should, in effect, be described by the following mesomeric formulas:

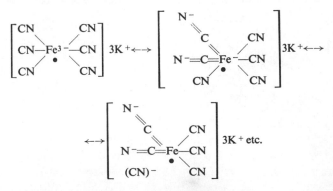

each of which contains an uncoupled electron.

Among the other important paramagnetic complexes we may mention: $[Cr(CN)_6]K_4$ containing two lone electrons, $[Co(H_2O)_6](NH_4SO_4)_2$ containing three lone electrons, $[Fe(H_2O)_6](NH_4SO_4)_2$ containing four lone electrons and $[FeF_6](NH_4)_3$ containing five lone electrons.

In contrast, the classic complexes such as $[Co(NH_3)_6]Cl_3$, $[Co(NO_2)_6]Na_3$, $[PtCl_6]K_2$, etc., are diamagnetic and do not possess free electrons.

Short Bibliography

M. BARRIOL, *Mécanique quantique*, P. U. F., Paris, 1951.

C. A. COULSON, *Valence*, Clarendon Press, Oxford, 1952.

M. J. S. DEWAR, *Electronic Theory of Organic Chemistry*, Clarendon Press, Oxford, 1949.

G. EMSCHWILLER, *Chimie physique*, 3 vol., P. U. F., Paris, 1951.

H. EYRING, J. WALTER and G. E. KIMBALL, *Quantum Chemistry*, John Wiley and Sons, N.Y., 1944.

S. GLASSTONE, *Theoretical Chemistry*, D. Van Nostrand, N.Y., 1944.

P. PASCAL, *Chimie générale*, 4 vol., Masson, Paris, 1950.

L. PAULING, *The Nature of the Chemical Bond*, Cornell Univ. Press, Ithaca, 1944.

B. PULLMAN and A. PULLMAN, *Les théories électroniques de la Chimie Organique*, Masson, Paris, 1952.

J. C. SLATER, *Quantum Theory of Matter*, McGraw-Hill Book Co., N.Y., 1951.

Y. K. SYRKIN and M. E. DIATKINA, *Structure of Molecules and the Chemical Bond*, Butterworth, London, 1950.

G. W. WHELAND, *Resonance in Organic Chemistry*, John Wiley and Sons, N.Y., 1955.

Index

INDEX

hydrogen—*continued*
  approximation, 11
hydrogenated substances, 48 ff.
hypsochromatic effect, 64

Index, bond, mobile, 57 ff.
  molecular, 67
  coordination, 74
  electric charge, 60
  energic, 56 ff.
  free valence, 59, 67, 69
  structural, 56 ff.
inert electron pair, 5
ion, 3 and *passim*
ionic formulas, 31
ionization potential, 38
  molecular, 61
isodensity contours, 26
isomer, d-cis, 60
  d-trans, 68
  s-cis, 68
  s-trans, 68
isomerism, cis-trans, 46

Kekulé formulas, 55 ff., 62
kinetic state of corpuscle, 6
Kossel, 4
K-region, 70 ff.

Langmuir, Irving, 4
Lavoisier, Antoine, 1
law, gravimetric, 1
  of conservation
    of energy, 7
    of mass, 1
  of definite proportions, 1
  of multiple proportions, 1
  of proportional numbers, 1
  volumetric, of chemical combination, 1
L.C.A.O.
  approximation, 24, 54
  function, 25
Le Bel, Joseph Achille, 3
Lewis, Gilbert N., 4, 5
linear combination of atomic orbitals, *see* L.C.A.O.
lithium, 18
localized bond, 41
London, Fritz, 28

Magnetic quantum number, 10
mass, law of conservation of, 1
matter, atomic theory of, 1
maximum
  overlapping, principle of, 33
  valence, 3
mechanics, wave, 1
Mendeleyev, Dmitri, 3
mesitylene, 72
mesomerism, 23 and *passim*
metals, alkali, 18
meta position
  of benzene, 65
  of substituents, 72
methane, 19, 45, 46
method, mesomerism, 23 and *passim*
  molecular orbitals, 23 and *passim*
methyl group, 70
mobile bond index, 57 ff.
model, carbon, 3
molecular
  bond index, 67
  ionization potential, 61
  model, flexibility of, 46 ff.
  orbitals method, 23 and *passim*
  reduction potential, 61
molecules, aromatic, 61 ff.
  conjugated, 41 and *passim*
  heteronuclear, 27 and *passim*
  homonuclear, 27 and *passim*
  non-conjugated, 41 and *passim*
  types, 2
moment, dipole, 60, 64, 72
  permanent, 37
Mulliken, 38
multiple proportions, law of, 1

Naphthalene, 57, 63, 64, 66–69
nickel, 77
  carbonyl, 77
nitrogen, 34, 45, 78
non-conjugated molecules, 41 and *passim*
non-localized bond, 41
normalization condition, 6
nucleus, 4 and *passim*
number, coordination, 74
  proportional, law of, 1
quantum
  azimuthal, 9
  magnetic, 10
  of spin, 15